THE TEMPER OF HERBS

The Temper of Herbs

Robert Allen Bartlett

OLYMPIA, WA
MMXX

Revelore Press
620 73rd Ave NE
Olympia WA 98506
USA

www.revelore.press

Book and Cover Design by Joseph Uccello.

ISBN 978-1-947544-32-1

Print edition first published by Revelore Press in 2020.

CONTENTS

ABSTRACT

THIS BOOK CONCERNS an on-going laboratory research project investigating the elemental and humoral constitution of medicinal herbs as given by classical sources. So, for example, when the Roman physician Claudius Galen or the renaissance herbalist Nicholas Culpeper say that Hemlock is an herb which is Cold in the 4th degree and Dry in the 3rd degree, we may have a method of confirming such a classification or of producing a classification if one does not exist. The determination of a medicinal herb's ability to affect the body and the relative intensity of that effect is a problem with a long pedigree of great minds in medicine, chemistry, and mathematics from ancient times to the present. The methodology of the present study employs modern thermogravimetric analysis combined with the classical "analysis by fire" or "spagyric anatomy" as described by alchemists from at least the time of Jabir ibn Hayyan (circa 800 CE) and which became the center of a great debate on the number and nature of the elements in the seventeenth century.

The text includes a short examination of the development of elemental theory as applied to medicine with an introduction to the four humors and humoral medicine practiced for over a thousand years, and is indeed still practiced in parts of the world. The main focus of interest is in how materials were tested in order to assign their temperament. The laboratory methods used in this study are fully explained with many graphic examples and comparisons between materials. The methods of data reduction used to arrive at a final value for a material's intensity are also explained for each phase of the investigation. Future possibilities are discussed and include the possibility of confirming classical designations for medicinal herbs and herbal compounds as well as application towards mineral medicines of the classical *materia medica*.

PREFACE

I T IS FUNNY how a single word can trigger a whole investigation into a subject, and that is certainly what happened here. While reading Avicenna's *Canon of Medicine*, concerning the melancholic humor or black bile that had become stagnant in the body, it was described as being like a *calx* or ash in the blood. That single word, calx, an old term used by the early alchemists to designate the ash of some material, suddenly brought to my mind the process of Fire Analysis or Spagyric Anatomy as practiced by the alchemists for centuries. Then, as C. A. Becker exclaimed in his work *Das Aceton*, all the parts fit.[1]

Humoral medicine describes the activity of four fluid-like substances in the body, each having an association with one of the classic four elements—Fire, Air, Water, and Earth—and together responsible for our health and temperament. The four humors—Blood, Yellow Bile, Phlegm, and Black Bile—were said to occur not only in the animal realm, but the vegetable and mineral realms had their analogous representatives. The alchemists describe methods for separating the elements from any body by a process of distillation. I had already distilled many herbs over the years using such methods, so I

---

1 C. A. Becker, *Das Aceton*, 1867.

was familiar with the process and products. My thought was, that by quantifying the "elements" of a plant obtained by the distillation, one might find a correlation to the temperament as assigned in the classical sources like Galen or Avicenna. What I mean by temperament is the ratio of the four elements in the body tested. The four elements, were themselves composed of the even simpler primary qualities: Hot, Cold, Wet, and Dry. The four elements, as distilled fractions from a plant, can thus be reduced to relative ratios of the primary qualities, and these ratios compared to the traditional classification such as Hot in the first degree and Dry in the third degree. Determining a medicine's intensity as measured along a scale of four degrees for each element has always been problematic, as there are no empirical methods recorded, only trials on patients carefully selected. The main intent of this research project was to unite humoral theory with alchemical theory using modern analytical equipment in order to develop a method whereby a medicinal plant could be analyzed to determine its humoral balance and intensity.

Part One: Theory

W E ARE TAUGHT in school that Hippocrates is the "Father of Modern Medicine," and yet as far removed in time as Hippocrates is from us, so too were the ancient Egyptian physicians from him. A thousand years before Hippocrates was even born, the ancient Egyptian physicians were compounding complex medical prescriptions and had achieved fame throughout the ancient world as the most skilled physicians.

Section of the Ebers Medical Papyrus circa 1550 BCE.

There is still much to discover in ancient Egyptian medicine. Currently, about 2,000 ancient Egyptian formulæ are known, and a quarter of them contain proportional measurements in the form of one or two fractional numbers following an ingredient. The precise identification of many of the plants remains under investigation and indeed some may no longer exist. Medicine in ancient Egypt recognized both the physical and non-physical constitution of man. In addition to the application of medicinal preparations they placed great confidence in the power of certain sounds or rhythms in the form of chants, spells, mantras, and incantations during the preparation and administering of the medicine. This was magical power they called "Heka."

The ancient Egyptians conceived the universe as being derived from a vast ocean, the "Waters of Nun"; within this ocean lived four divine couples in perfect harmony. No one took precedence over another, and so all was fleeting and potential. In one version of the story, Thoth, god of wisdom, spoke words that moved the waters and began the creation of the universe and everything in it. The goddess Maat, consort of Thoth, was assigned the duty of maintaining the balance of forces—of light and dark, good and bad, pure and impure—lest all of creation collapse again into a watery chaos.

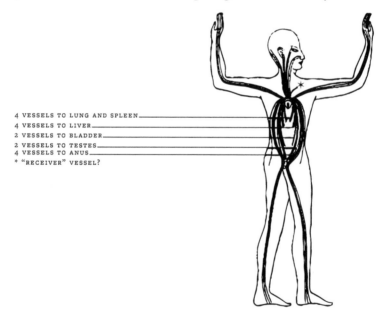

4 VESSELS TO LUNG AND SPLEEN
4 VESSELS TO LIVER
2 VESSELS TO BLADDER
2 VESSELS TO TESTES
4 VESSELS TO ANUS
* "RECEIVER" VESSEL?

The life giving waters of the Nile were ever present in the minds of the Egyptians, and they saw a corollary in man. During irrigation of crops, if a channel becomes clogged, the section denied water suffers.

Keeping the channels open and freely flowing with life-giving water was the key to healthy life in the fields. Man was seen to be similarly composed of various ducts and channels that take in nutrient and remove wastes.

Egyptian preventative medicine was concerned with keeping open and flowing the system of "Metu," (vessels or channels) which mainly carry four vital fluids; air, water, food (contained in the blood), and waste products.

Maintaining the balance of Maat, separating the good from the bad, the pure from the impure, reached into all aspects of life. Purging oneself three days each month was a common practice according to the ancient historian, Herodotus. They believed that toxins from food residues were a major cause of illness if left inside too long and thus the importance of keeping things moving in their proper channels.

Canopic jars. Author photo.

In the process of mummification, four of the internal organs were removed and treated separately then placed into the four so-called "canopic jars." Each of these organs were said to be under the protection of one of the four sons of Horus, Lord of the Earth, and each of these in turn under the protection of one of the great goddesses associated with the cardinal points of the compass, the four supports of heaven. The perception of a fourfold influence in Nature is prominent in Egyptian philosophy and mysticism. Around 1550 BCE, an unprecedented development appeared in Egyptian medicine: precise measurements of individual ingredients in prescriptions, especially those intended for internal use.

One of the great myths of the Egyptians describes how Set, god of chaos and corruption, was locked in battle with Horus, defender of light and cosmic harmony. In the bloody duel, Set plucked out one of Horus' eyes and tore it into pieces. The great god Thoth, Lord of all Wisdom, used his own magical power, his Heka, to reunite the pieces of the eye and make it whole again. The eye of Horus—now called "The Whole Eye"—became a symbol for wholeness and health. We see a shadowy reminder of this in the current symbol used to designate a medical prescription.

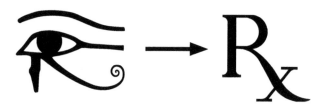

In Egyptian hieroglyphic writing, the six portions of the eye of Horus which were torn off by Set were used to designate fractional quantities. The physicians of the time used these fractional notations to proportion ingredients of a prescription in order to "fill the eye" and bring about the "Whole Eye" or health to the patient. On adding the fractions of the eye together, one finds that there are only $63/64$ths. The final $1/64$th was said to be added by Thoth and is the Heka, the magical power of the compounder.

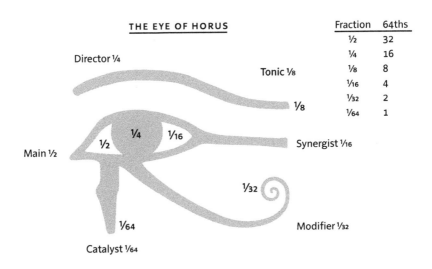

Figure shows a proposed use of the eye fractions for compounding an herbal medicine.

The Egyptian *materia medica* included about 800 medicinal substances derived from the vegetable, animal, and mineral realms. Prescriptions ran from the simple to the very complex in formulations. One famous preparation is Khyphi, a complex blend of herbs, resins, honey and wine used mainly as an incense to fumigate an area for sacred works; but also used as a medicine internally and externally. The preparation required about a year and was considered important enough to be inscribed on the temple walls of Edfu and Esna. There is some speculation that Khyphi served as the model for what later was known as Theriac, an important panacea of the Middle Ages and into the Renaissance and a subject that will come up later.

Egyptian medicine treated not only the physical body; they also recognized man's subtle constitution as well. In life, there were methods used within the temples such as guided meditation, aromatherapy, and dream cultivation to treat certain psychological problems; but even in death there were treatments necessary to insure a healthy afterlife.

The Papyrus of Ani, Chapter 89[2]

The physical body was known as the "Khat," denoted by a dead fish because it was liable to putrefaction in the same way a dead fish goes bad easily. We noted above the removal of the organs placed into canopic jars; this was only one step in the preparation of the deceased body, a process that required 72 days to complete. Meanwhile, as the body is prepared, the more subtle aspects of the deceased are detained through the use of magical and ritual techniques. The Egyptians recognized many parts to our subtle constitution, but the most important were the "Ba" and the "Ka" of the individual. The Ba represented all of those attributes that make us unique, our character, our soul. The Ka represented our share of life-force, the universal energy that makes all actions possible, the Spirit. These two can take on an autonomous existence and drift away in the netherworld, but

2   http://www.bardo.org/ani/

they could also be retained by magical operations and purified in the process. Finally, if all of the preparations go well, the Ba and Ka are reunited to become an "Ahku," or "Glorified Being" and access is granted to the now prepared body through the performance of "The Opening of the Mouth" ceremony which will allow the deceased to travel at will between the worlds. Strange as it all sounds, we will come upon these ideas again when we discuss alchemical development later and especially what is known as the "spagyric method."

HUMORAL MEDICINE

The Egyptians heavily influenced the development of both Greek philosophy and medicine. The early pre-Socratic philosophers visited Egypt, studied in its temples, and applied their rational approach to understanding the true nature of reality. In perhaps a restatement of the Egyptian Waters of Nun, Thales postulated that Water was the source of all creation. Others suggested Air or Fire as the source; but it was Empedocles in the fifth century BCE who is credited with listing the four elements, Fire, Air, Water, and Earth as the components of all that is created and his contemporary Zeno of Elea postulated the four primary qualities, Hot, Cold, Wet, and Dry.

Around 500 BCE, Alcmaeon of Croton combined these ideas on the fourfold nature of reality with the medical arts by introducing the idea that health depended on a perfect balance or harmony of these basic qualities inside the human body. However, the first formulation of the humoral theory of medicine is to be found in the so-called Corpus Hippocraticum, a collection of writings and fragments attributed to Hippocrates.

Hippocrates

The name Hippocrates has become associated with the beginning of ancient medicine. He is called "The Father of Medicine" and "Prince of Physicians," and today, our physicians still adhere to the Hippocratic Oath. Born on the island of Cos in 460 BCE, he was the eighteenth lineal descendant from Asclepius, the patriarch of a long family line of healers. Hippocrates was a contemporary of Socrates, Democritus, and Herodotus and adopted the four element theory to medicine in such a concise and practical manner, it became the dominant cosmological model for at least the next fifteen centuries.

Hippocrates postulates a principle that he calls "physis," which pervades all of material creation, and which serves as the motive power of elementary matter. This principle is the cause of animal life and motion, and through it, the blood and spirits receive heat, life and sensation,

> ...for in the body are many constituents, which, by heating, by cooling, by drying or by wetting one another contrary to nature, engender diseases; so that both the forms of diseases are many and the healing of them is manifold.[3]

> The body of man has in itself blood, phlegm, yellow bile and black bile; these make up the nature of his body, and through these he feels pain or enjoys health. Now he enjoys the most perfect health when these elements are duly proportioned to one another in respect of compounding, power and bulk, and when they are perfectly mingled. Pain is felt when one of these elements is in defect or excess, or is isolated in the body without being compounded with all the others.[4]

3 Hippocrates, *On the Nature of Man*, Ch. 3-4.
4 *Ibid.*

Aristotle

Aristotle is credited with describing the four temperaments for the first time.

He describes the four principle qualities in his work, *On Generation and Corruption*. They are quite different from how we would describe the terms today:

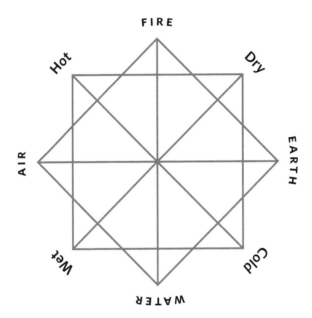

Aristotle's Elements

PRIMARY QUALITIES

Hot	Separates by bringing things of a like nature together. Expansive and Centrifugal.
Cold	Unites by forcing to the center, Contraction, Centripetal.
Wet	Allows adaptation to environment.
Dry	Forms boundaries and limits.

COMPOUNDING OF QUALITIES

Hot	Cold	Wet	Dry
Fire	Air	Water	Earth
Blood	Yellow Bile	Phlegm	Black Bile
Sanguine	Choleric	Phlegmatic	Melancholic
△	△	▽	▽

INNATE HEAT △   RADICAL MOISTURE ▽

Galen

It was the Greek physician Galen of Pergamon who, in the second century CE, systematized all of the previous medical concepts and created a new theoretical system that became the model of medicine until well into the seventeenth century.

GALENIC MEDICINE

Vital Spirit	Heart	Sun	Hot & Dry
	LIFE, LIGHT, AND MOTION TO THE BODY		
Natural Spirit	Liver	Jupiter	Hot & Moist
	NOURISH THE BODY. GENERATION OF THE FOUR HUMORS		
Animal Spirit	Brain	Mercury/Moon	Cold & Moist
	INTELLECT AND SENSORY FUNCTIONS		

The Natural Spirit nourishes the body throughout as the Vital Spirit quickens it, and the Animal Spirit gives it sense and motion. The Natural Faculty or Virtue resides in the Liver, and is generally governed by Jupiter, Quasi Juvans Pater; its office is to nourish the Body and is dispersed through the body by the veins. From this are bred four particular Humors, Blood, Choler, Phlegm, and Melancholy.

Blood is made of Meat perfectly concocted, in quality hot and moist, governed by Jupiter: it is by a third concoction transmuted into Flesh, the superfluity of it into Seed, and its receptacle is the Veins, by which itis dispersed through the Body. Choler is made of Meat more than perfectly concocted; it is the spume or froth of blood: clarifies all the Humors, heats the Body, nourisheth the apprehension, as Blood doth the judgment.

It is in quality hot and dry; fortifieth the attractive faculty, as Blood doth the digestive moves man to activity and valour: Its receptacle is the Gall, and is under the Influence of Mars.

Phlegm is made up of Meat not perfectly digested; it so fortifies the virtue expulsive, as makes the Body slippery, fit for ejection: it fortifies the brain by its consimilitude with it; it spoils Apprehension by its Antipathy to it. It qualifies Choler, cools and moistens the heart: thereby sustaining it, and the whole Body, from the fiery effects, which continual motion would produce: Its receptacle is the Lungs, and is governed by Venus, some say by the Moon, perhaps it may be governed by them both: it is cold and moist in quality.

Melancholy is the sediment of Blood, cold and dry in quality, fortifying the Retentive Faculty, and memory ; makes them sober, solid, staid, and fit for study ; stayes the unbridled toyes and fooleries of lustful thoughts, and reduceth them home to the Centre it is like a grave Councellor to the whole Body: Its receptacle is in the Spleen, and it is governed by Saturn. Of all these Humours, blood is the chief, all the, rest are but superfluities of blood ; yet are they necessary superfluities, for without any of them man cannot live. Namely, Choler is the fiery superfluity: Phlegm, the Watery: Melancholy, the Earthly.[5]

The exact combination and proportions of the four humors in the body are said to give rise to an individual's "Temperament" or "Complexion." Galen lists nine temperaments, four with a prevalent quality such as Hot, Cold, Wet, or Dry; another four with two qualities in harmony as Fire, Air, Water, or Earth. The final one on the list is of a perfectly balanced composition of the four elements.

---

5 Nicholas Culpeper, *Pharmacopoeia Londinensis* (Boston, 1720), A4.

THE FOUR HUMORS

Humor	Qualities	Element
Sanguine	Hot & Wet	Air
Choleric	Hot & Dry	Fire
Phlegmatic	Cold & Wet	Water
Melancholic	Cold & Dry	Earth

THE PROPERTIES OF MEDICINAL
MATERIALS

Galen examined the properties of simple drugs (a medicine composed of a single vegetable, mineral, or animal substance) and made a distinction between two different kinds of properties: qualities and faculties. Qualities meant a drug's primary elemental qualities: Hot, Cold, Wet, and Dry. These were also referred to as manifest qualities. The terms "complexion," "temperament," or "nature" indicate the balance of these qualities. Faculties, "powers." or "virtues" refer to the many different effects a drug appeared have on the body. Classifying these properties took the form of describing the different tastes of drugs, their operations in the body, and the application of reason, experience, and common sense.

The faculties of drugs were divided into primary, secondary, tertiary, and quaternary faculties. The primary faculties were the powers produced by the qualities: warming, cooling, drying, and moistening—most often in orders of strength or degrees from one to four. A medicine which is in the first degree changes the body from its normal state, but not in an obvious manner. In our bodies, the innate heat is about in the first degree, and medicines add to or subtract from this. So a hot medicine in the first degree would simply nourish the natural heat of the body without adding to or decreasing it. A medicine of the second degree causes obvious changes in the body, but not in a very violent manner. A third degree medicine affects the body with violence, but not in a very dangerous manner, while a fourth degree medicine produces dangerous change. These are the primary faculties of medicines and of primary importance to our present study of plant materials.

The secondary faculties are described as rarefying, opening, thinning, attracting, repelling, densifying, closing, thickening, mollifying, hardening, causing to adhere, diluting, binding, pulling or drawing, wiping off or dispelling, obstructing, hurting, and purifying. The secondary faculties of simple drugs were distinguished from each other by the way they acted in the body as well as the consistency of their material and the amount of dryness, warmth, moistness, and cold present in them. Matter could be thick or thin. Simples were thin if they could easily be broken into smaller parts, whereas thick, hard, solid, and tough simples were not particularly brittle. Simples that rarified, opened, thinned, and attracted, acted then by uniting heat and thin matter. Repelling, dense making, closing and thickening occurred when thickness was joined with coldness; the power of mollification when moistness came with this thickness and cold; of hardening if it were accompanied by dryness instead of moistness. The secondary faculties originated in the temperament of a drug.

ELEMENTAL DEGREES

Hot		
	4th	Burning
	3rd	Warming
	2nd	Thinning
	1st	Opening

Cold		
	4th	Anodyne
	3rd	Thickening
	2nd	Cooling
	1st	Refreshing

Since it was obvious that some Hot drugs were "hotter" than others (such as cinnamon versus jalapeno pepper) and similar relations existed for Cold, Wet, and Dry medicines, Galen established a system of four degrees for each of the four primary qualities. Thus we could have a drug which is not only known to be hot; we could specify the relative amount of "hotness," for example Hot in the third degree.

We can use a Cartesian grid to help illustrate and visualize these concepts. The vertical or active axis represents the four degrees of Hot and Cold and the horizontal axis, the four degrees of Wet and Dry. The origin of the grid represents a "temperate" point where all four primary qualities are balanced; so a person or medicine which is temperate has no excess of Hot, Cold, Wet, or Dry. Such a person was considered the perfect test subject for determining the temper of a medicine under trial since they were poised to be influenced by the qualities of the medicine quite readily. A First Degree medicine would elicit a faint response just barely noticeable and a Fourth Degree medicine would be four times as strong.

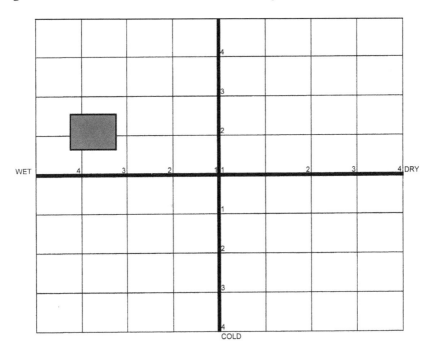

Example above indicates Hot in the Third Degree and Wet in the Second Degree. In this study, the designation would be represented as H3W2.

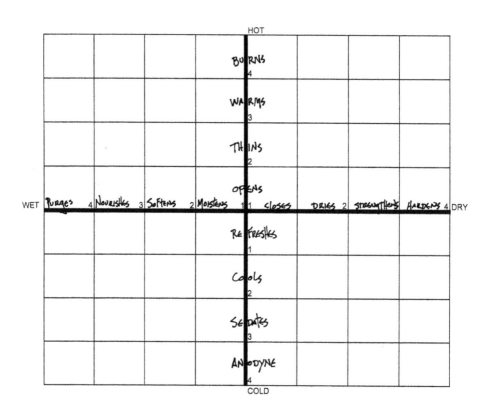

Secondary Faculties of medicinal herbs by degree of intensity

Using the same grid system we can arrange a selection of medicinal herbs by their temper and intensity as given by three traditional sources:

Summa Medicinae
Albuzale De Simplicibus
Culpeper

	WET 4	WET 3	WET 2	WET 1	DRY 1	DRY 2	DRY 3	DRY 4
HOT 4					ASAFETIDA			Garlic, B.Pepper, Asafetida, Onion, Yarrow, Mustard, Hellbore
HOT 3	Basil		Garlic, Galbanum	Turmeric	Ginger, Parsley	Mugwort, Rue, Caraway, Anise, Hyssop, Dill, Juniper, Cumin, Thyme, Cloves, Sage		
HOT 2		Satyrion	Elecampane, Bdellium	Basil, Southernwood, Fennel	Aloe, Fennel, Calamus, Melissa, Dill, Basil, Elder, Betony, Myrrh, Cardamom, Scammony, Cannabis, Mastic	Cinnamon, Anise, Horehound, Sage	Fenugreek	
HOT 1			Borage, Tragacanth, Gum Arabic, Licorice, White Sugar	Chamomile, Root, Saffron, Pine, Horsetail, Linseed, Senna, Fenugreek, Fumitory	Agaric, Mugwort, Wormwood, Honey, Rose, Storax, Agrimony	Absinthium, Aloe, Dock		
COLD 1			Mallow, Violet, Alkanet	Violet, Clovers, Lettuce, Spinach, Cucumber sd, Archangel, Olive oil, Melon sd, Hemp	Alkanet, Rose, Yarrow, Myrobalan AB3, Coriander	Oak		
COLD 2		Prune, Psyllium, Alder, Birch			Plantain, Acacia, Pomegranate, Houseleek, Myrobalans AB3, Myrrh, wh.Poppy, Mastic, Trag.	Acacia, Sumac		
COLD 3	Chickweed	Purslane, Teasle, Cucumber sd					Camphor, Teasle, Shepherds purse, Sumac, Willow, Comfrey	
COLD 4		Poppy			Henbane		Hemlock	Nightshade

HOT (top) — COLD (bottom); WET (left) — DRY (right)

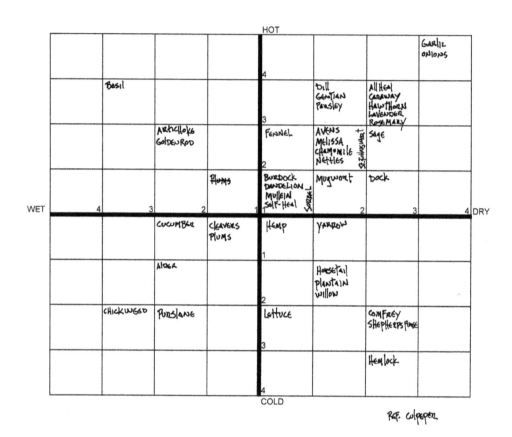

A selection of herb temperaments from Nicholas Culpeper.

GALEN'S RULES FOR ESTABLISHING A MEDICINE'S INTENSITY

In diagnosing temperament, it was necessary to know the means of each axis in order to determine when the quality was in excess. This was done by physical examination and inspection. Further, Galen argued, the mixture of the four elements in the body could be best assessed by examining the skin. By nature, the skin gave the best evidence of a balanced mixture of the four qualities. For example, everything harder than the skin (like bones, nails, corns, hair) tended to be dry while everything softer than the skin (blood, phlegm, fat, brain) tended to be moist. Galen pointed out that the palm has a relatively balanced amount of Hot, Cold, Wet, and Dry and is the best place for assessing the blend of humors in the individual.[6]

The balance of an individual does not depend upon the elements and qualities being exactly equal, but upon being distributed in such a manner that the resulting equilibrium or temper of the body as a whole is the most appropriate for that individual. In his work, "On Temperaments," Galen describes the state of "eucrasia" as being the perfect balance of the four qualities;

> The best temperate man is he who in the body seems to be in the mean of all extremities, that is skinniness and fatness, heat and coldness...and regarding the body this is the best temperate man. Similarly in his soul he is in the middle of boldness and timidity, of negligence and impertinence, of compassion and envy. He is cheerful, affectionate, charitable and prudent.[7]

Disease results from an imbalance in the activity of the Four Humors, which Galen called "dyscrasia."

CURE THROUGH OPPOSITES

> You may make the mixture of them (simples) in what form you please; only for your better instruction at present, accept of these few Rules:
>> 1. Consider, That all Diseases are cured by their contraries, but

---

6 Robert M. Stelmack and Anastasios Stalikas, "Galen on the Humour Theory of Temperament." *Personality and Individual Differences* 12.3 (1991): 255-63.

7 *Ibid.*

All parts of the Body [are] maintained by their likes. Then if heat is the cause of the disease, give the cold Medicine appropriated to it; If Wind, see how many Medicines appropriated to that Disease expel wind, and take them.

2. Have a care you use not such Medicines to one part of your body which are appropriated to another; for if your brain be over-heated, and you use such Medicines as cool the Heart or Liver, you may make matters worse.

[...]

6. Consider the Natural temper of the part of the Body afflicted and maintain in that, Else you extinguish Nature, as the Heart is hot, the Brain cold, or at least the coldest part of the Body.

7. Observe this general Rule That such Medicines as are hot, in the first degree, are most habitual to our Bodies, because they are just of the heat of our Body.[8]

MAN THE MICROCOSM

Determining the individual temperament is necessary. Astrology is an objective method.

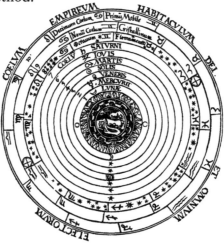

---

8 Culpeper, *Pharm. Lond.* epistle.

From Claudius Ptolemy's *Tetrabiblos*:

But, I think, just as with prognostication, even if it be not entirely infallible, at least its possibilities have appeared worthy of the highest regard, so too in the case of defensive practice, even though it does not furnish a remedy for everything, its authority in some instances at least, however few or unimportant, should be welcomed and prized and regarded as profitable in no ordinary sense. [...]

Recognizing, apparently that these things are so, those who have most advanced this faculty of the Art, the Egyptians, have entirely united medicine with astronomical prediction. For they would never have devised certain means of averting or warding off or remedying the universal and particular conditions that come or are present by reason of the ambient, if they had had any idea that the future cannot be moved and changed. But as it is, they place the faculty of resisting by orderly natural means in second rank to the decrees of fate, and have yoked to the possibility of prognostication its useful and beneficial faculty, through what they call their iatromathematical systems (medical astrology), in order that by means of astronomy they may succeed in learning the qualities of the underlying temperatures, the events that will occur in the future because of the ambient, and their special causes, on the ground that without this knowledge any measures of aid ought for the most part to fail, because the same Ones are not fitted for all bodies or diseases; and, on the other hand, by means of medicine, through their knowledge of what is properly sympathetic or antipathetic in each case, they proceed, as far as possible, to take precautionary measures against impending illness and to prescribe infallible treatment for existing disease.[9]

---

9 Claudius Ptolemy, *Tetrabiblos*, Book 1, Ch. 3.

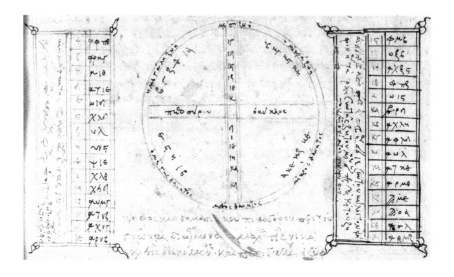

The Circle of Petosiris showing an example of Alexandrian
Iatromathematics using astrology to predict the course and outcome
of an illness. MSGrec2419, Bibliothèque nationale de France.
Département des manuscrits.

Calculation of Temperament from the natal chart
according to Ptolemy

We must, then, in general observe the eastern horizon and the planets that are upon it or assume its rulership in the way already explained; and in particular also the moon as well; for it is through the formative power of these two places and of their rulers and through the mixture of the two kinds, and furthermore through the forms of the fixed stars that are rising at the same time, that the conformation of the body is ascertained; the ruling planets have the most power in this matter and the special characters of their places aid them.

The detailed account then, as one might report it in simple terms, is this; First, among the planets, Saturn, if he is in the orient, makes his subjects in appearance dark-skinned, robust, black-haired, curly haired, hairy-chested, with eyes of moderate size, of middling stature, and in temperament having an excess of the moist and cold. If Saturn is setting, in appearance he makes them dark, slender, small, straight-haired, with little hair on the body, rather graceful, and black-eyed; in temperament, sharing most on the cold and dry.[10]

PLANET	ORIENTAL	OCCIDENTAL
Saturn	Cold & Wet	Cold & Dry
Jupiter	Hot & Wet	More Wet
Mars	Hot & Dry	Mostly Dry
Venus	Hot & Wet	More Wet
Mercury	Mostly Hot	Mostly Dry

Paul of Aegina, known by the Latin, Paulus Aegineta, was an Alexandrian physician born around 625 CE and one of the last of the ancient Greek medical encyclopaedists. His *Medical Compendium in Seven Books*, or *Epitomae medicae libri septem*, collected together Greek and Roman medical knowledge of the time. His work later translated into Arabic had a powerful influence on the development of Arabic medicine and that influence lasted well into the medieval period when the Arabic texts were translated into Latin. The first two sections of Book 7, which is the *materia medica*, are useful to our present study. Section one describes testing a substance to determine properties and temperament using taste as the guide. Section Two presents a description of the medicinal effect produced by the four degrees of each elemental quality.

---

10   *Ibid.*, Book 3, Ch. 11.

SECT. I.
ON THE TEMPERAMENTS OF SUBSTANCES
AS INDICATED BY THEIR TASTES

It is not safe to judge from the smell with regard to the temperament of sensible objects; for inodorous substances consist indeed of
thick particles, but it is not clear whether they are of a hot or cold
nature; and odorous substances, to a certain extent, consist of fine
particles and are hot; but the degree of the tenuity of their parts, or
of their hotness, is not indicated, because of the inequality of their
substance. And still more impracticable is it to judge of them from
their colours, for of every colour are found hot, cold, drying, and
moistening substances. But in tasting, all parts of the bodies subjected to it come in contact with the tongue and excite the sense,
so that thereby one may judge clearly of their powers in their temperaments. Astringents, then, contract, obstruct, condense, dispel,
and incrassate; and, in addition to all these properties, they are of a
cold and desiccative nature. That which is acid, cuts, divides, attenu-
ates, removes obstructions, and cleanses without heating; but that
which is acrid, resembles the acid in being attenuant and purging,
but differs from it in this, that the acid is cold, and the acrid hot; and,
further, in this, that the acid repels, but the acrid attracts, discusses,
breaks down, and is escharotic. In like manner, that which is bitter
cleanses the pores, is detergent and attenuant, and cuts the thick
humours without sensible heat. What is watery is cold, incrassate,
condenses, contracts, obstructs, mortifies, and stupefies. But that
which is salt contracts, braces, preserves as a pickle, dries, without
decided heat or cold. What is sweet relaxes, concocts, softens, and
rarefies: but what is oily humectates, softens, and relaxes.[11]

11   Paulus Aegineta, *The Seven Books of Paulus Aegineta*. Trans.Francis Adams, (London: Sydenham
Society, 1847), Book 7, Sec. 1,2

SECT. II.
ON THE ORDER AND DEGREES OF THE TEMPERAMENTS

A moderate medicine which is of the same temperament as that to which it is applied, so as neither to dry, moisten, cool, nor heat, must not be called either dry, moist, cold, or hot; but whatever is drier, moister, hotter, or colder, is so called from its prevailing power. It will be sufficient for every useful purpose to make four ranks according to the prevailing temperament, calling that substance hot, according to the first rank, when it heats, indeed, but not manifestly, requiring reflection to demonstrate its existence: and in like manner with regard to cold, dry, and moist, when the prevailing temperament requires demonstration, and has no strong nor manifest virtue. Such things as are manifestly possessed of drying, moistening, heating or cooling properties, may be said to be of the second rank. Such things as have these properties to a strong, but not an extreme degree, may be said to be of the third rank. But such things as are naturally so hot as to form eschars and burn, are of the fourth. In like manner such things as arc so cold as to occasion the death of a part are also of the fourth. But nothing is of so drying a nature as to be of the fourth rank, without burning, for that which dries in a great degree burns also; such are misy, chalcitis, and quicklime. But a substance may be of the third rank of desiccants without being caustic, such as all those things which are strongly astringent, of which kind are the unripe juice of grapes, sumach, and alum.[12]

12   *Ibid.*

JABIRIAN ALCHEMY

Fall of the Byzantine Empire and transmission of medical knowledge to the Arab world

A bū Mūsā Jābir ibn Hayyān's theory of transmutation of metals is based on Aristotle's theory of metallic generation involving the "Two Exhalations," the vaporous and smoky; but Jabir has revisioned them as Mercury and Sulfur. Mercury carries the Cold/Wet qualities and Sulfur the Hot/Dry qualities. Under the influence of the planets, the metals are formed in the womb of the earth by combinations of Mercury and Sulfur in varying proportion and quality. The metals only differ according to accidental qualities brought out by the mixture of impure Sulfurs and Mercuries.

Jabir characterized the metals as having both exterior qualities and interior qualities. Two of the elementary qualities resided on the outside and two qualities were hidden within.

METAL	EXTERIOR QUALITIES	INTERIOR QUALITIES
Lead	Cold/Dry	Hot/Wet
Tin	Cold/Wet	Hot/Dry
Iron	Hot/Very Dry	Cold/Wet
Gold	Hot/Wet	Cold/Dry
Copper	Hot/Dry	Cold/Wet
Mercury	Cold/Wet	Hot/Dry
Silver	Cold/Dry	Hot/Wet

Gold alone was held to have the most subtle, pure, and equilibrated nature and this explained its freedom from corrosion, a sickness the other metals suffered from in various forms and degrees. "If one wishes to convert silver into gold, it is necessary first to push back the coldness into the interior so that the heat can appear. Then it is necessary to push back the dryness into the interior so that the humidity can appear. In this way silver can be transformed into gold."[13] Jabir's ideas on metallic transmutation directly tie into humoral medicine. Just as the physician cures diseases by applying drugs of contrary qualities, so the alchemists prepared medicines to cure metals of their "leperous" disorders. These medicines are the famed "Elixirs" of transmutation, the most famous being the Philosophers Stone of the alchemists.

Jabir maintains that the Elixir can be produced from materials in all three kingdoms of nature, animal, vegetable, or mineral. The separation of substances into their constituent elements and natures, treated in detail in *The Seventy Books*, takes place by means of a special distillation. The distillation of a substance began at a low temperature and slowly ascended to a red heat. Jabir saw this as the decomposition of the body into its constituent elements. Unlike Aristotle, Jabir associated the elements with an "undetermined substance," like a blank slate or medium, to give materiality to the elements and qualities. As the distillation proceeded, a liquid substance separated out first, which for Jabir was the Water element, and formed part of the composition of the body. Next, a gaseous substance distills and produces a liquid Jabir calls oil or grease and names it as the Air of the material. Finally a combustible liquid distills over and Jabir labels it as the Tincture or Fire element. The residue remaining in the bottom of the retort is identified as the Earth element.

Fire	=	Hot	+	Dry	+	Substance
Air	=	Hot	+	Wet	+	Substance
Water	=	Cold	+	Wet	+	Substance
Earth	=	Cold	+	Dry	+	Substance

13 Paul Krause, "Jābirian Alchemy (A Translation of the Introduction and Chapter One, Section One of *Jābir Ibn Ḥayyān: Contribution to the History of Scientific Ideas in Islam: Jābir and Greek Science*)," International Journal of Shī'ī Studies 4.2 (2006): 195-220. Translated from French by Keven Brown.

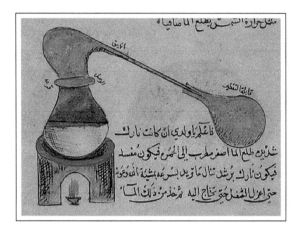

*An eighth-century illustration of the distillation
process by Jabir ibn Hayyan.*

JABIR'S ELEMENTAL COMPOSITIONS

"...despite Aristotle's warnings to the contrary, he (Jabir) confounds matter and substance, thus rendering matter a 'this something'; he then makes the four primary Aristotelian qualities (Hot, Cold, Wet, Dry) concrete, independent and corporeal entities."[14] Jabir proceeds to give directions for isolating the individual qualities, Hot, Cold, Wet, and Dry, by treating the distilled elements with suitable agents and processes. For example, Jabir suggests using mineral sulfur, which has a strong Dry nature, to balance and remove the Wetness of the Water element, leaving only pure Cold.

Jabir would prepare a different type of Elixir for each specific metallic body. These Elixirs were created from mixtures of the four qualities and four elements which correspond to the constitution of the bodies to which they were applied and, in effect, "curing" them of their imbalance. Jabir describes nine operations to prepare an Elixir:

---

14   Syed N. Haq, *Names, Natures and Things* (Springer, 1994), 49.

Selection of a favorable time for the work. Here astrological considerations of both agent and patient were involved.

The First Distillation—Separation of the four elements from which the subject matter is composed.

Purification of the Water—Reduction of the element to Coldness

Purification of the Oil—Reduction to its Wetness only

Purification of the Fire—Reduction leaving only the Hot quality

Purification of the Earth—Reduction to Dryness

Determination of the "Weights" with which it is suitable to compose the Elixir based on the "weights" of the subject to be acted upon

Mixture again of the natures—not by juxtaposition but by total mixture

Application of the Elixir—Projection on metals for transmutation

Jabir adopted Galen's four elemental degrees and expanded upon the idea. Now each element had four degrees and each of the degrees had seven subdivisions giving a total of 28 divisions per element or 112 in total for all four elements:

✳   ✳

✳

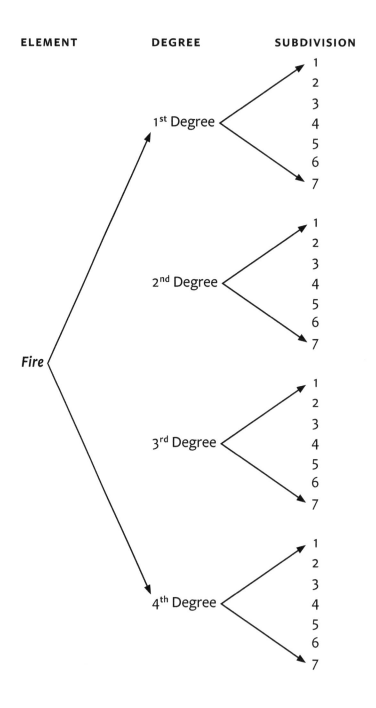

The importance of the number 28 is that it is also the number of Arabic letters. Jabir assigned a letter to each division from the beginning of the alphabet to the end, repeating the order Hot, Cold, Dry, Wet. The divisions allowed a much more precise classification of the elemental qualities and this was essential for both cultivating the Elixir and determining the excesses or deficiencies in a given body. Only after the weights of these natures were known could the alchemist turn to the main task of reducing or increasing them as necessary. A medicine could now be described as being in the beginning, middle, or end of a degree.

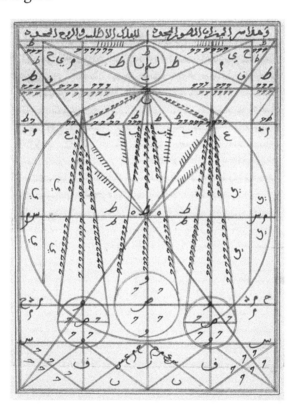

Diagram from Kitāb al-Burhān fī asrār ʿilm al-mīzān (Proof Regarding the Secrets of the Science of the Balance) *by al-Jaldakī (d. 1342).*

Calculation of a material's temper by Jabir involved a mixture of Pythagorean mathematics, Gematria, where numbers and letters are in-
terchangeable, and reference to additional tables of weighted factors
to arrive at a result.

AVICENNA 980–1037 CE

Medicines have four grades of potency. Grade I drugs are those
which, in specified doses, do not produce any appreciable effect on
the body, for instance, heat or cold produced by them is not felt at all
unless the drug is taken repeatedly or in large doses. Grade II drugs
are those which are a little more potent than Grade I but are neither
so potent as to produce any visible disturbance in the functions of
the body nor do they per se interfere with the normal course of physiological functions except secondarily. It is only when administered
repeatedly in larger doses that they produce any visible damage or
disturbance of normal functions. Grade III drugs are those which in
specified doses produce per se notable disturbance of normal functions of the body but not to the extent of producing disease or death
unless taken repeatedly or in larger doses than normal. Grade IV
drugs are those which produce damage or destruction of the body.
This action refers to poisonous drugs which act by their characteristic qualities but a substance which is lethal by its specific nature is
a true poison.[15]

Determination of temperaments of simple drugs through experiment

The potency of drugs can be determined in two ways: (1) by analogy
and (2) by experiment. Let us begin with the latter (i.e. experiment).

15   Avicenna, *Canon of Medicine, Book I* (New Delhi, India: Hamdard University, 1998), sec. 15.

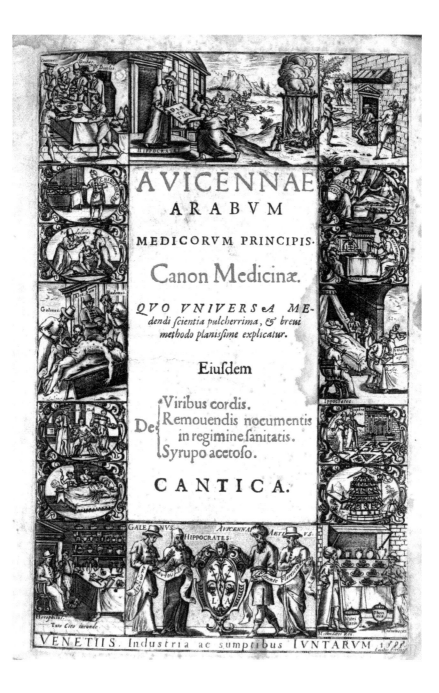

AVICENNAE
ARABVM

MEDICORVM PRINCIPIS.

Canon Medicinæ.

QVO VNIVERSA ME-
dendi scientia pulcherrima, & breui
methodo planissime explicatur.

Eiusdem

Viribus cordis.
De { Remouendis nocumentis
in regimine sanitatis.
Syrupo acetoso.

CANTICA.

VENETIIS. Industria ac sumptibus IVNTARVM 1595.

We say that experiment can give us an authentic account of the potency of a drug if certain rules are observed:

1. The drug should be free from an extensive alteration, whether it be accidental heat or cold or a quality which is due either to some sort of transformation taking place in the drug or it may be the combination of something else with it. You may observe that water, though intrinsically cold, becomes hot when placed on fire. On the other hand, gum euphorbium is intrinsically hot, yet it may turn out to be cold when it is cooled. Almond is intrinsically moderate and rarefied, but when rotten, becomes very hot. Fish is basically cold but when salt is applied to it, it becomes very hot.

2. The experiment should be based on simple diseases; if the disease is the result of two causes demanding two different treatments and the experiment of a drug on both of them has become successful, it would be difficult to determine the (exact) cause of success.

3. The drug may be tried in heterogeneous diseases. If the drug proves to be useful in all of them, it would not be proper to say that the drug has got an opposing temperament, for it might have been useful in the case of a particular disease intrinsically and in the case of another disease extrinsincally. Such being the case our experiment would not assure us of the hot or cold nature of the drug unless we are in a position to distinguish between the intrinsic act of the drug from its extrinsic one.

4. The drug should be, both qualitatively and quantitatively, in proper proportion to the nature and severity of the disease. There are some drugs the degree of the heat of which falls short of the degree of cold of certain diseases. It is, therefore, necessary to try a drug initially in milder degrees and then gradually proceed till the potential of the drug is known.

5. The time when the drug has proved effective should be noted. If the effect appears soon after the administration of the drug, one may unhesitatingly conclude that the effect is natural to the drug. On the other hand, if the effect observed in the beginning is in sharp contrast to that observed in the last round of the experiment, or the

drug remains inactive at the outset but acts at the end only, then it would be a doubtful and difficult case.

6. The action of the drug should be constantly watched to find out whether the action is one and the same in all or in most of the cases. If it is not so, the action may be regarded as temporary and accidental because innate qualities of a substance do emanate therefrom perpetually or at least in most cases.

7. The experiment should be made on a human body. If it is made on some other (animal) body, the result may be different for two reasons: (i) The drug which is hot in relation to human body may possibly be cold in respect of the body of a lion or a horse; the drug may be warmer than human body but colder than the body of a lion or a horse. Therefore Himalyan rhubarb which, I think, is very cold for the body of a horse though it is hot for the human body. (ii) A drug may have one property in relation to one body and quite another in regard to another body. For example, aconite is a poison for the human body but it is not so for that of a starling. These are the rules which must be observed while investigating into the properties of drugs through experiment.[16]

Determination of Drug Temperament by Analogy

As for other rules, one which must be known to physicians, is that a salty, sweet, bitter or pungent tastes must necessarily be of warm substances. Whereas the tastes that are astringent, sour or acrid must belong to cold substances. Likewise, strong and acute odours can exist with a warm substance only. White colours of thickened bodies with some humidity would always be found in cold substances.

If these colours belong to dry and husky bodies, they must be associated with hot substances. For black colour, in both cases mentioned above, the condition would be opposite because cold whitens

16   Avicenna, *Canon II*, Sec. 2, 5-7.

the most and blackens the dry whereas heat blackens the moist and whitens the dry.

Odours which come next to tastes in importance and colours (to which the above rule could be applied) occupy the last place. One of the reasons why tastes override odours is that the former are felt just when they meet the faculty of perception. As such, these are the best of all constitutents of a drug to communicate a quality while odours and colours show their effect even when these are not in contact with the constitutents of the drug. It is possible that some vapours emanating from the rarefied parts of the drug is felt; whereas no vapour arises from the heavy parts of that drug. Similarly, a colour which is perceptible may possibly be the colour of the dominating exterior and not of the hidden dominated part of the drug.[17]

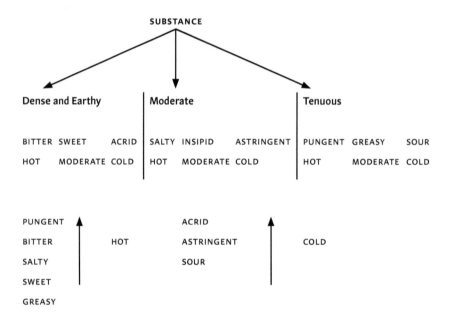

17   Avicenna, *Canon II*, 9–10.

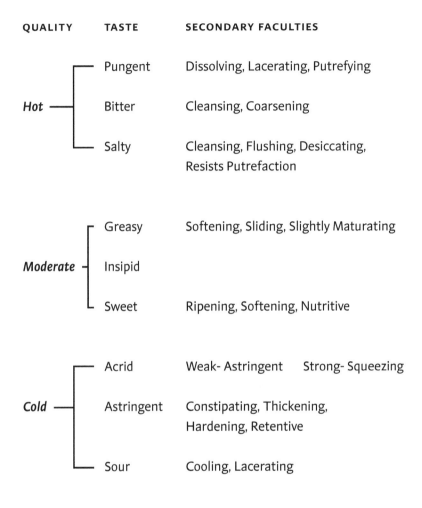

QUALITY	TASTE	SECONDARY FACULTIES
Hot	Pungent	Dissolving, Lacerating, Putrefying
	Bitter	Cleansing, Coarsening
	Salty	Cleansing, Flushing, Desiccating, Resists Putrefaction
Moderate	Greasy	Softening, Sliding, Slightly Maturating
	Insipid	
	Sweet	Ripening, Softening, Nutritive
Cold	Acrid	Weak- Astringent Strong- Squeezing
	Astringent	Constipating, Thickening, Hardening, Retentive
	Sour	Cooling, Lacerating

In our discussion of Galen earlier, he cautions us in one of his simple rules, to use a medicine that is of the proper temper for the organ or system treated. You do not want to unduly cool an organ that should be hot or dry an area that should be kept moist. Avicenna provides us with a listing of the various parts of the body and their relative Hot, Cold, Wet, and Dry qualities. The graphic below makes it easier to visualize the tempers of the body's components based on *The Canon*, Book one, Section two.

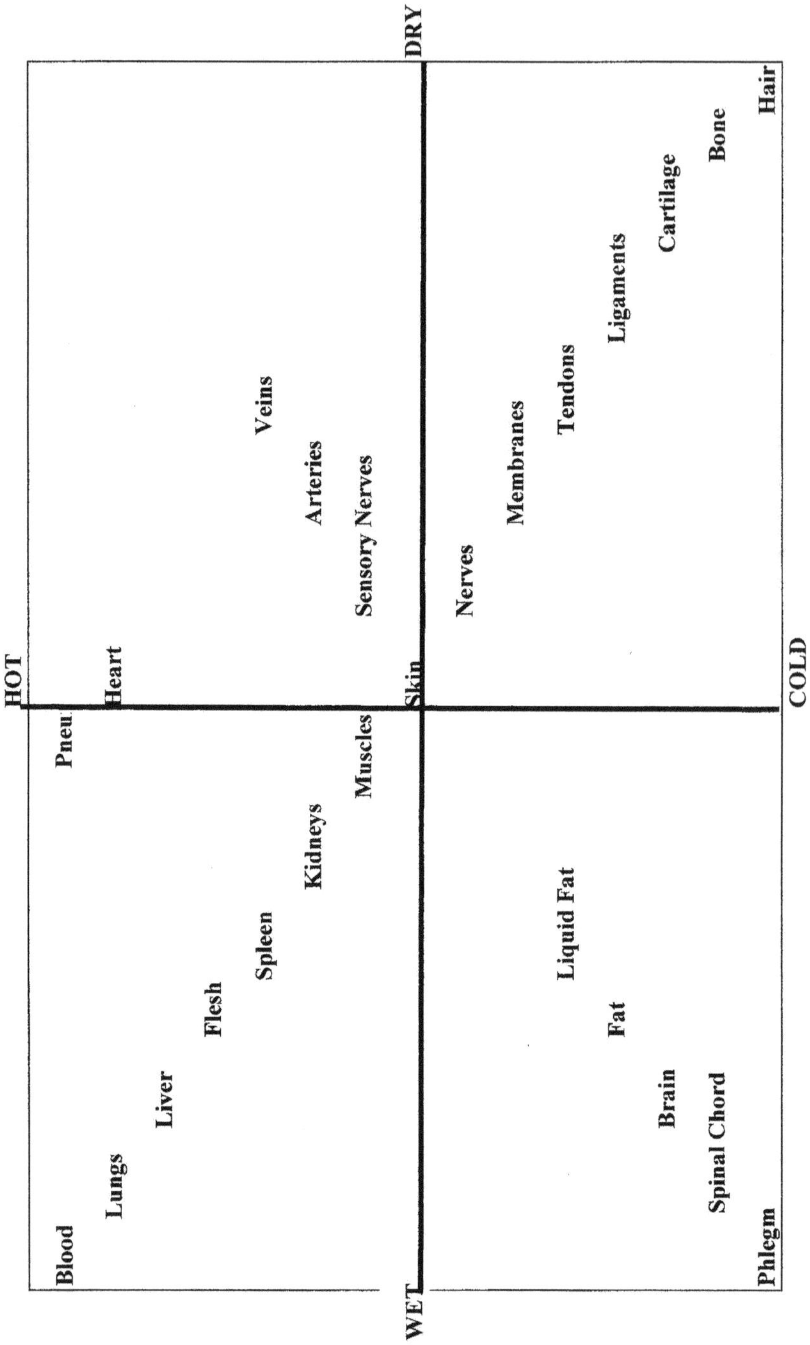

DRY

HOT

COLD

WET

Skin

Blood
Lungs
Liver
Flesh
Spleen
Kidneys
Muscles
Pneu
Heart

Sensory Nerves
Arteries
Veins

Nerves
Membranes
Tendons
Ligaments
Cartilage
Bone
Hair

Spinal Chord
Brain
Fat
Liquid Fat
Phlegm

The healthy body maintains a humoral balance generally within the first degree of each of the four qualities, so the graphic above indicates relative Hot, Cold, Wet, and Dry properties of the internal organs all within the first degree. Some authors place the normal range for the body at the second degree. Hair was considered to be the coldest and driest part of the body while Phlegm is coldest and wettest. The skin is placed in the position of balance and, as Galen mentioned, can indicate the type of imbalance should an illness arise.

Avicenna writes an interesting line relevant to our study in this section. In defense of his assignment of hair being drier than bone he says, "When we take bone and hair in equal quantity and distill them in an alembic, comparatively more water and oil flow from the bone and there is little residue. Thus bone is moister than hair." The process of analyzing drugs through distillation, as we saw earlier with Jabir, has a long and often overlooked history; we will discuss this aspect in much greater detail later as it proved to be a vital aspect of the current research project.

MEDIEVAL MEDICINE

OF THE FOUR HUMORS IN THE HUMAN BODY

FOUR humors form the body in this style,
Atrabilis, Blood, Phlegm and yellow Bile.
With earth atrabilis may well compare.
Consuming fire with bile, and blood with air;
Blood is moist, warm, and vital as the air;
While phlegm is cold, through water's copious share;
Bile burns like fire, where'er it flows along;
Gall, dry and cool, to earth bears likeness strong.

The Sanguine temperament
Such are by nature stout, and sprightly too,
And ever searching after gossip new.
Love Venus, Bacchus, banquets, noisy joy,
And jovial, they kind words alone employ;
In studies apt—pre-eminent in arts.
No wrath from any cause e'er moves their hearts.
Gay, loving, cheerful and profuse in all,
Hearty, tuneful, wherever fate may call;
they're florid, bold, and yet benign withal.

The Bilious temperament
WITH headstrong people yellow bile sorts well,
For such men would in everything excel.
They learn with ease—eat much and grow apace.
Are great, profuse, and avid of high place.
Hairy, bold, wrathful, crafty, lavish, shrewd,
Their form, is lithe, complexion saffron-hued.

The Phlegmatic temperament.
PHLEGM breadth imparts, slight power and stature short,
Forms fat, and blood of an inferior sort.
Such men love ease, not books—their bodies steep,
And heavy minds and slothful lives in sleep.
Sluggish and dull their senses almost fail;
They're fat, to spitting prone; their mien is pale.

The Melancholic temperament.
OF dark Atrabilis we've next to learn
Which renders man sad, base and taciturn;
In studies keen, in mind not prone to sleep.
In enterprise unfaltering to keep.
Doubting, artful, sad, sordid misers, they
Are timid, while their hue resembles clay.[18]

DIET

Let food be your medicine.
—Hippocrates

In as much as the bodies of human beings are always subject to dissolution, namely because they have Innate Heat and owing to the
warmth of the air which surrounds them, they need to replace that
which is dissolved from them. Therefore bodies need to eat and to
drink, and the faculty of appetite was placed in them so as to know
the right time to eat, and the right quantity to take and the kind of
food they need.

This being so, someone who wishes to preserve his health should
pay attention to two things; First, that the food he ingests be suitable to replace what was dissolved from his body, and, second that

18 *Regimen sanitatis Salernitanum*, trans. Thomas Paynell (1528).

he expel from the body the residues of the food that are formed in it. You should therefore have knowledge of the different natures of the foods and of the different natures of the bodies and their characteristics so that you may know the suitability of every kind of food for each kind of human being.[19]

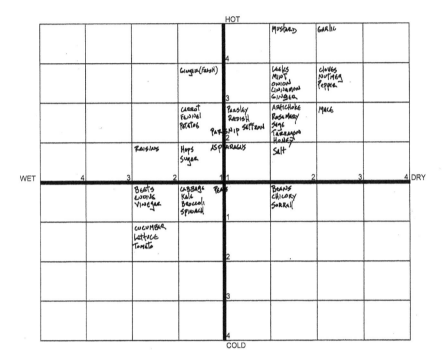

Table showing a selection of food items from Castel of Helth *by Sir Thomas Elyot.*

General effects of food according to modern Unani medicine:

Proteins can be heating or cooling but always drying, likewise Carbohydrates can heat or cool but are always moistening. Fats are warming and moistening while Water is of course cooling and moistening.

---

19 Galen, *On Regimen.*

Most of the minerals are cold and dry but there are a few that warm and dry.

HOT

	4 (WET)	3	2	1		1 (DRY)	2	3	4
4	BANANAS DATES GUAVA MANGO	ARTICHOKE ASPARAGUS CHIVES OLIVES	BREAD Bulgar-wheat FLOUR MACARONI	GOAT GOOSE LAMB LIVER MUTTON					
3	PEACHES RHUBARB — ALMONDS	SPINACH SPRING ONIONS SQUASH	Noodles Pasta RYE BREAD SPAGHETTI	TURKEY CHEESE GHEE COND. MILK					
2	BRAZIL NUTS PISTACHIOS SUNFLOWER SEED	BISCUITS CAKE CHOCOLATE LICORICE	wheat ALL BRAN FLAKES BRAN OATS	FRESH CREAM LECITHIN MARGARINE MAYONAISE					
1	HONEY MOLASSES SUGAR		PUFFED WHEAT	PEANUT BUTTER olive oil sunflower oil					
WET / DRY									
1						APPLES AVOCADOS CHERRIES 1 COCONUT	CABBAGE CAULIFLOWER CELERY EGG PLANT	BARLEY BEANS (all) CORN COUSCOUS	BEEF FISH (ALL) PORK VEAL
2						GOOSEBERRIES GRAPEFRUIT KUMQUATS 2 LEMON	GREEN BEANS MUSHROOMS PEAS POTATOES	LENTILS LINSEED MAIZE MILLET	SOUR CREAM LARD YOGHURT COFFEE
3						LIME ORANGES PLUM (SOUR) 3 POMEGRANATE	SAUERKRAUT DRIED TOMATOES SWEET POTATOES TOMATOES	POPCORN POPPY SEED SESAME SEED CORN FLAKES	FIZZY DRINKS BALSAMIC VINEGAR WINE VINEGAR PICKLES
4						PRUNES RASPBERRIES STRAWBERRIES	COCONUT oil CORN oil PEANUT oil SESAME oil	PEANUTS	VINEGAR

COLD

Hot and Wet foods (upper left) to balance the Cold and Dry Melancholic humor (lower right) and conversely Cold and Dry foods to balance the Hot and Wet Sanguine humor.

RENAISSANCE ASTROLOGERS

Consider that all Time is measured out by
Motion, and that the Original of all Motions is in the
Heavens, for it is the Motion of the Sun which causeth
Day and Night, Summer, Winter, Spring, & Harvest;
From which conversion of Times and Years, all changes
proceed, both Heat and Cold, Dryness, and Moisture:
by which four is caused Life and Death, Generation &
Putrefaction, encrease & decrease of Elementary things;
for the Elementary World is the Womb of all Elementary
Creatures, both Animals, Minerals, and Vegetables,
it conceives them and nourishes and cherisheth
them being conceived.[20]

From ancient traditions to modern scientific studies, we know that medicinal herbs have physiological effects on specific organ systems. Herbs, like the organs they affect, are considered to fall under the influence of a particular planet or sign of the zodiac on the basis of an affinity. Each planetary sphere has a unique energetic expression and signature qualities associated with it, such as color, musical tones, parts of the body, diseases, medical effects, herbs, stones and metals. For example, the planet Venus is said to be the "ruler" of the metal copper metal and the herb Yarrow (among many others), as well as affecting the kidneys in humans. This rulership is a two-way interaction called sympathy, and refers to the planetary energies as they affect our world, and things of this world manifesting the different qualities of these planetary energies.

Nicholas Culpeper (1616–1654) was an English botanist, herbalist, physician, and astrologer. His published books include *The Eng-*

20 Culpeper, *Pharm. Lond.* epistle.

lish Physician (1652) and the *Complete Herbal* (1653), which contain a rich store of pharmaceutical and herbal knowledge of the period. Culpeper spent the greater part of his life in the English outdoors cataloging hundreds of medicinal herbs and making the preparation of medicines easy for the common people. He followed Galen's humoral medicine and was a staunch supporter of astrological medicine, believing astrologers the only ones fit to practice the art of medicine.

The following "Degrees of Medicine" are quoted directly from the 1653 edition of *Culpeper's Herbal* as many of his descriptions of the uses of plants provide references to the degrees of hot or cold, dry or moist characteristics of the plant. His descriptions provided one of the main sources for comparison of properties in this study.

> The degrees then of temperature are to be diligently heeded, which ancient physicians have concluded to be four in quantities, viz. heat and cold, of each we shall speak a word or two severally.
>
> I. All medicines simply considered in themselves are either hot, cold, moist, dry, or temperate. The qualities of medicines are considered in respect of man, not of themselves; for those simples are called hot, which heat our bodies; those cold, which cool them; and those temperate which work no change at all in them, in respect of either heat, cold, dryness, or moisture. And these may be temperate, as being neither hot nor cold; yet may be moist or dry; or being neither moist or dry, yet may be hot or cold: or, lastly, being neither hot, cold, moist, nor dry.
>
> II. In temperature there is no degree of difference; the differences of the other quantities are divided into four degrees, beginning at temperature; so that a medicine may be said to be hot, cold, moist, or dry, in the first, second, third, or fourth degree. The use of temperate medicines is in those cases where there is no apparent excess of the first qualities, to preserve the body temperature, to conserve strength, and to repair decayed nature. And observe, that those medicines which are called cold, are not so called because that they are really cold in themselves, but because the degree of their

heat falls below the heat of our bodies, and so only in respect of our temperatures are said to be cold, while they are themselves really hot; for without heat there would be no vegetation, springing, nor life.

III. Such as are hot in the first degree, are equal heat with our bodies, and they only add a natural heat thereto, if it be cooled by nature or by accident, thereby cherishing the natural heat when weak, and restoring it when it is wanted. Their use is, 1. To make the offending humors thin, that they may be expelled by sweat or perspiration. 2. By outward application to abate inflammations and fevers by opening the pores of the skin. 3. To help concoction, and keep the blood in its just temperature.

IV. Such as are hot in the second degree, as much exceed the first, as our natural heat exceeds a temperature. There use is, to open the pores and take away obstructions, by cutting tough humors through, and by their essential force and strength, when nature cannot do it.

V. Such that are hot in the third degree are more powerful in heating, they being able to inflame and cause fevers. Their use is to provoke sweat or perspiration extremely, and cut tough humors; and therefore all of them resist poison.

VI. Such that are hot in the fourth degree do burn the body if outwardly applied. Their use is to cause inflammations, raise blisters, and corrode the skin.

VII. Such as are cold in the first degree, fall as much on the one side of temperature as hot doth on the other. Their use is 1. To qualify the heat of the stomach, and cause digestion. 2. To abate the heat in fevers; and, 3. To refresh the spirits, being suffocated.

VIII. Such as are cold in the third degree are such as have repercussive force. And their use is 1. To drive back the matter, stop defluctions; 2. To make the humors thick; and 3. To limit the violence of choler, repress perspiration, and keep the spirit from fainting.

IX. Such as are cold in the fourth degree are such as stupefy the senses. They are used 1. In violent pains; and 2. In extreme watchings, and the like cases, where life is despaired of.

X. Drying medicines consume the humors, stop fluxes, stiffen the parts and strengthen the nature. But if the humidity be exhausted already then those consume the natural strength.

XI. Such as are dry in the first degree strengthen; in the second degree bind, in the third, stop fluxes, but spoil the nourishment, and bring consumptions; in the fourth, dry up the radical moisture, which being exhausted, the body must needs perish.

XII. Moist medicines are opposed to drying, they are lenitive, and make slippery. These cannot exceed the third degree: for all things are either hot or cold. Now heat dries up, and cold congeals, both which destroy moisture.

XIII. Such are moist in the first degree, ease coughs, and help the roughness of the windpipe; in the second, loosen the belly; in the third, make the whole habit of body watery and phlegmatic; filling it with dropsies, lethargies, and such like diseases.

XIV. Thus medicines alter according to their temperature, whose active qualities are heat and cold, and whose passive qualities are dryness and moisture.

XV. The active qualities eradicate diseases, the passive are subservient to nature. So hot medicines may cure the dropsy, by opening obstructions; the same may also cure the yellow jaundice, by its attractive quality in sympathizing with the humor abounding: and contrariwise cold medicines may compress or abate a fever, by condensing the hot vapors, and the same may stop any defluxion or looseness.

The Astrological Man from Très Riches Heures du Duc de Berry
(1412–1416) by the Limbourg brothers.

Temperaments of the Planets		Temperaments of the Zodiac Signs	
Jupiter	Sanguine	Air signs	Hot/Wet
Sun, Mars	Choleric	Fire signs	Hot/Dry
Saturn, Mercury	Melancholic	Earth signs	Cold/Dry
Moon, Venus	Phlegmatic	Water signs	Cold/Wet

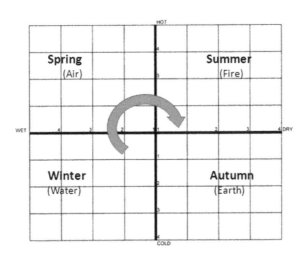

TEMPERAMENTS OF THE SEASONS

As the Earth moves through the year, it changes complexion. We are intimately connected to the Earth and its many cyclic activities. During the seasonal changes we are most vulnerable to disturbances in our humoral balance.

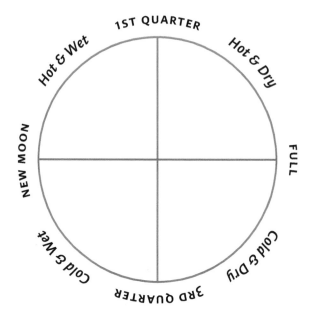

Lunar Influence.

Ptolemy recognized that the planets change temperament as they progress around the zodiac and especially notes whether they rise before the sun (oriental) or after the Sun (occidental). Astrologer Richard Saunders, provides the temperament changes of each planet as it passes through each sign of the zodiac in his work, *The Astrological Judgment and Practice of Physic*, of 1677. For example, the normally Cold and Dry Saturn becomes Hot and Wet in the sign of Libra the traditional sign of his exaltation.

> And here note, that these four elements, twelve signs, and seven planets do induce in all mortal bodies four humors, viz. blood, which is sweet, choler, which is bitter, melancholy, which is sour, and phlegm, which is saltish: but these four humors are so united in the body of man, and mixed and knit in such sort, that there is no separation thereof until the dissolution of the body, and separation of the

spirit from the body, *the which dissolution is done in many ways;*[21] but here it is to be understood but of one way, that is by natural death, and not by unnatural death; and according to that humor which is most prevalent and prominent in the body of man, thereafter is the

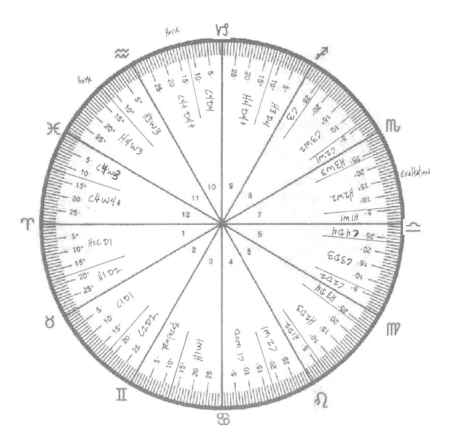

Temper of Saturn through the signs.

man called, either sanguine, choleric, phlegmatic, or melancholic, and every one of these humors have their proper times of rule, and different times of working in their several times, as occasion is given. Their general times of distinct rule, as thus; Sanguine rules from 9 at

---

21   As in alchemy. Emphasis mine.

night till 3 in the morning, Choler from 3 to 9 fore-noon, Melancholy from 9 to 3 afternoon, Phlegm from 3 to 9 at night.'[22]

Again, the proportion of medicine and of the body, and the degree of the disease and of medicine, and commixtion of humours, and the diversity thereof, are not known by any means but by astronomy; for who can make a just proportion of medicine for any disease, except he be a good astronomer?[23]

According to astrologer William Lilly, one may calculate one's temperament from the natal horoscope as follows:

FACTOR	EXAMPLE		
Ascendant Sign	Sagittarius (Fire)	Hot	Dry
Ascendant Lord	Jupiter	Hot	Wet
Ascendant Lord's Sign	Libra (Air)	Hot	Wet
Season	Winter	Cold	Wet
Moon Sign	Virgo (Earth)	Cold	Dry
Moon Phase	Full to		
	3rd quarter	Cold	Dry
Moon Aspects			
(opp Mars in Pisces)	Mars	Hot	Dry
	Pisces	Cold	Wet
Planets in 1st House	N/A		
"Lord of Geniture"	Saturn	Cold	Dry
	Totals	4 Hot/5 Cold	4 Wet/5 Dry
	Final	1 Cold	1 Dry
	Melancholic		

22   Richard Saunders, *The Astrological Judgment and Practice of Physick* (1677; Bel Air, MD: Astrology Classics, 2005), 96.
23   *Ibid.*, 80. (old copy)

·GALENVS ⁝ AVICENA ⁚ ƲPOCRATES

MODERN VIEWS
PHYTOCHEMISTRY

Plants produce what are termed "primary" and "secondary" metabolites in their life cycle. The primary metabolites comprise the bulk of a plant and include all of those materials necessary for the plant to develop and grow. These include the various proteins and genetic materials in cells and the starches, cellulose, and lignin supporting the structure. The secondary metabolites, while not essential to the plant's lifecycle are developed by the plant to provide protection against the elements, attack by outside predators, as well as suppressing mold, and fungal growth. They can also help the plant to heal if it is injured and send out chemical messages to insect allies in order to promote reproduction by pollination.

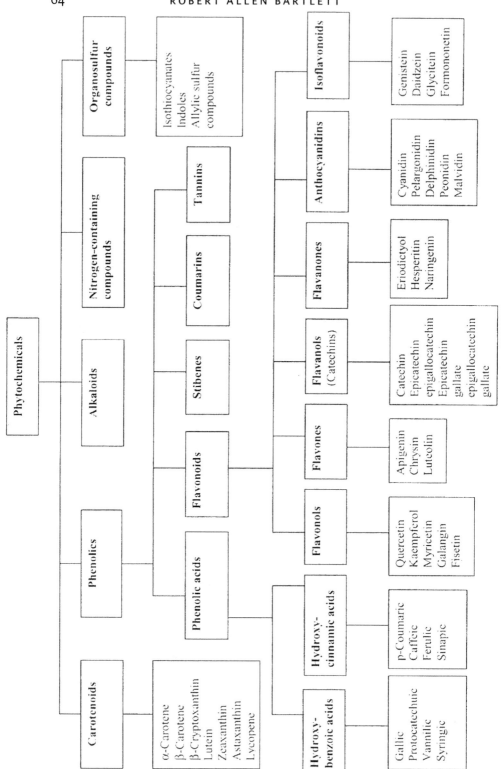

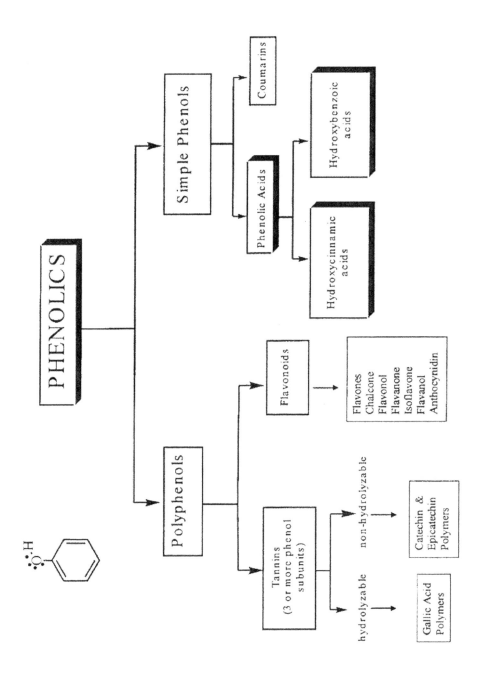

Secondary metabolites can be generally divided into four major classes of related compounds as terpenoids, alkaloids, Phosphorus and nitrogen containing compounds, and the largest class phenolics which include flavonids, tannins, and coumarins; all very powerful medicinal agents.

Mankind discovered long ago that that the chemicals developed by plants to protect and heal themselves could be used in the human body to affect a similar response and thus herbal medicine was born.

VEGETABLE KINGDOM

PRIMARY   SECONDARY

LIFE PROCESSES   PROTECTION

STRUCTURE

HOT

Volatile Oils
Terpenes
Bitter Aromatics
Resins
Coumarins

Carbohydrates
WET   Fixed Oils   Tannins   DRY
Mucilages
Water   Flavonids
Cyanogenic
Gycosides
Limonene
Fruit Acids

COLD

Mathew Wood's placement of phytochemical activities
(not arranged by relative intensity).

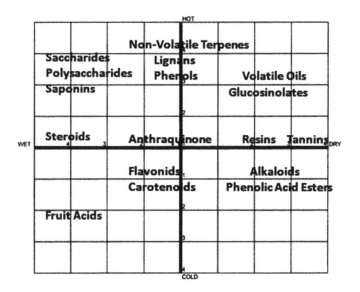

University of Tehran placement of phytochemical activities
(not arranged by relative intensity).

Using statistical analysis of traditional Persian medicine designation of plant tempers and modern chemical profiles of the selected plants, a study in 2013 concluded that, "Glucosinolates and sulfur-containing phytochemicals were estimated hottest while fruit acids, flavonoids, phenolic esters and polyene-carotenoids coldest. Similar estimations were performed for dry and wet primary qualities showed Glucosinolates and resins as driest and anthraquinones and iridoides wettest phytochemicals."[24]

24   Farid Ramezany, et.al. "Primary Qualities in Phytotherapy and Traditional Medicines: A Statistical Study," *Journal of Drug Delivery and Therapeutics* 3.3 (2013): 1-6.

	HOT	
Sanguine		**Choleric**
Sweet		**Pungent**
Unctuous		**Acrid**
WET		DRY
Sour		**Astringent**
Salty		**Bitter**
Phlegmatic		**Melancholic**
	COLD	

Tastes, placed according to Theophrastus, Aristotles successor, correspond well with the above placement of phytochemicals. The hot spicy taste of many foods is due to the presence of glucosinolates and volatile oils, saccharides are sweet, and fruit acids sour. Most of the alkaloids like cocaine and the opiates are intensely bitter and astringent.

FIRE PHILOSOPHERS

Now I will teach and describe the secret of the arts, which secret is
at the heart of all secrets hidden in the art of alchemy; since one will
here understand the wonderful works that God has accomplished
in all things he has made out of the four elements... For I shall here
teach you to know the spirits of herbs, trees, and all growing things;
how to separate them from their bodies, and also how to purify the
four elements and restore them to their first being and their perfect
power; that is, that when the elements are purified, how they can
be put together again and make a perfect and fixed body of them,
which is then glorified and has a miraculous effect.

—ISAAC HOLLAND, *OPERA VEGETABILIA* (15th CENTURY)

S
O, how does alchemy fit into this discussion? There are so
many ideas, opinions and conjectures as to just what alchemy is all about; is it proto-chemistry or pseudo-science, a
spiritual path or a psychological metaphor, fact or fiction?
This debate is nothing new, it has been going on for centuries and
yet alchemy continues to fascinate all who venture into its dark waters. Part of the problem lies in the literature itself which is filled with
symbol, myth, metaphor, and analogy. If you lack a proper key, it is
easy to become lost in a labyrinth of uncertainty and despair. Another part of the problem with understanding the intentions of alchemy
is that it crosses all the artificial lines that have become enmeshed
in modern society. The lines between science, magic and religion, or
mind and matter take on a whole new dimension within the Hermetic Corpus.

Alchemy has been called the perennial philosophy, Sacred Science, and Divine Art; going in and out of vogue for centuries, and
so it is today that the study of alchemy is gaining worldwide interest

in both popular and academic circles. There exists a massive body of alchemical information available to all like at no other time in history. Indeed histories are being rewritten without the biases of past interpretations, and much of what we were taught about the pseudo scientific or fraudulent nature of alchemy are now seen as false or at least incomplete descriptions.

Alchemy has been called the search for perfection and the search for the quintessence. The origins of alchemy are still the center of hot debate with China, India, and Egypt as major contenders. East and West certainly influenced the development of core alchemical theories. For the West, alchemy is considered to be the product of ancient Egyptian technical skills and mysticism with Greek philosophy that took place around 200 BCE in Alexandria.

The ancient Greek philosophers, most of whom studied for many years in the Egyptian mystery schools, sought to clarify and summarize the nature of reality, how things come into existence and ultimately decay. Alchemists from all ages say we must follow in the footsteps of nature for "Our Art" to be successful and the concepts of nature from such great luminaries as Pythagoras, Socrates, Plato, and Aristotle held full sway over alchemical thought well into the eighteenth century.

Some of the most important ideas from Greek philosophy which helped shape the theory and practice of alchemy include foremost the concept that all we perceive in our everyday world is derived from one source. "One is All" became a fundamental mantra and stable foundation for the development of philosophies concerned with the operations of Nature. The idea that all things are moving toward a state of greater perfection is another central concept throughout the alchemical corpus, today we might think of this as the force of natural evolution. Closely related to this are the recurring themes of the celestial ascent of the soul and the separation of souls from bodies.

The concept of four elemental states and a trinity of powers within the One resulted in a conception of the elemental constitution of materials as embodiments of those spiritual principles and set the stage for development of ideas concerning transmutation from one material into another with its ultimate perfection in mind. The ancient philosophers postulated an infinite ocean of living mind containing the forms of all creation in potential. All of the elemental qualities within the One in total balance, no one taking precedence over another, static, nothing can happen and in a sense it does not really exist. The ancients called this the One, the All, Chaos, Divine Intellect, Prima Materia, Celestial Fire and many other similar titles. We can symbolize the concept but cannot comprehend this state of unity.

The One, reflecting on itself, begins the first motion towards polarity and thereby to expressing itself. Now we get contrast. One pole compared to the other or acting on the other is the condition required for us to understand. Modern science recognizes the unity of energy and matter which the ancients described as Spirit and Matter or Aristotle's Form and Matter. Matter did not really exist until it was impressed with a Form or more exactly a Substantial Form (from which we derive our term, substance). This Form was the real Soul of the thing not just how it looked but the formative energy behind its entire life cycle and purpose for being. But Form and Matter are codependent; one does not exist without the other. The One becomes two and the three aspects together become the fundamental package of essentials for a thing to exist. At its highest level of expression, this is the trinity inherent within the One; expressing the divine attributes of omniscience, omnipotence and omnipresence. The One as ultimate Spirit or intellect has within itself an energetic mode and material mode, the three being anciently designated as Spirit, Soul, and Body—or as the alchemists termed them Mercury, Sulfur, and Salt. To the alchemist, everything that exists possesses a body, soul and spirit; even those things we don't usually associate with such concepts as a plant or lump of rock. In modern terms, we might describe these three essentials as matter, energy, and intelligence.

The familiar hermetic axiom "As above, so below" from the Emerald Tablet of Hermes Trismegistos guides us to an understanding that these spiritual principles have their reflection here in the material world with affinities to certain types and states of matter. Nature is a continuum from the most dense to the most subtle essences, and the ancient hermetic philosophers perceived the cyclic process of Nature whereby One becomes the many and the many return to the One.

The physical world is just one layer (the most dense or fixed part) of a much larger macrocosm which includes layers of spiritual intelligence or archetypal forms, rational and instinctive levels of mind, as well as an electromagnetic signature. Greek philosophy mentions these various levels as the Intellectual world, the Celestial world, and the Elemental world; while the cabbalistic student refers to four interconnected worlds of increasing subtlety. In the East, Indian alchemists speak of the several sheaths or subtle bodies which enclose a spark of the divine present in all things; each sheath rooted in a different level of reality.

One of the most important goals of the alchemical work is the perfection of an incorruptible body, which gold represents for the metallic realm. Variously termed the "Spiritual Body," the "Diamond Body," "Glorified Corpus," and "the Immortal Body" it is the true Form of the individual. From the most ancient times, preservation or mummification of the physical body in order to provide a deceased entity an access to the physical world has been practiced worldwide. Early alchemical investigators sought out methods of creating an incorruptible body of spiritualized matter that could be occupied while still here, alive and coextending a physical body.

Which brings us to the laboratory works of the alchemist. Some will contend that there is no real laboratory tradition in alchemy that it's all about psychology and metaphor. However it then becomes difficult to explain the existence of alchemical laboratories distributed throughout the world. That the alchemists were working with material substances in a unique manner has been indicated by numerous studies and authors. Was it just protochemistry? In some cases, yes, but there has always been a line of alchemists guided by a more esoteric philosophy, the philosophy of Nature from the alchemical viewpoint.

The alchemical laboratory is a place where theory is put to the test. Very often insights into the workings of nature are very deeply impressed in the mind of the worker because seeing the changes that occur in the laboratory to the work at hand provides powerful sub-conscious messages which are processed and lead to further insights and illumination of the work. The key process or method used in the laboratory is based on nature's own process in the macrocosmic world. This process was termed *Spagyria* by Paracelsus, derived from Greek words meaning to separate and reunite, which is a rewording of the older alchemical adage *solve et coagula*.

In his writings, Paracelsus outlines the nature of the physical representatives of spiritual principles or the physical cloaks of non-physical realities to be met with in the laboratory, he says:

> Everything which is generated of its elements is divided into three, namely into Salt, Sulfur, and Mercury. Learn the form which is peculiar to these three. One is liquor and this is the form of Mercury; one is oiliness and this is the form of Sulfur; one is alkali and this is the form of Salt.[25]

> Now I am come to the arts, and I shall begin from Distillation an invention of later times, a wonderful thing, to be praised beyond the power of man, not that which the vulgar and unskillful man may use. For they do but corrupt and destroy what is good. But that which is done by skillful artists. This admirable art, teaches how to make spirits, and sublime gross bodies, and how to condense, and make spirits become gross bodies. And to draw forth of plants, minerals, stones and jewels, the strength of them, that are involved and overwhelmed with great bulk, lying hid, as it were, in their chests. And to make them more pure, and thin, and more noble, as not being content

---

25 Paracelsus, quoted in Robert Allen Bartlett, *Real Alchemy* (Lake Worth, FL: Ibis, 2009), 33.

with their common condition, and so lift them up as high as heaven. We can by Chymical Instruments, search out the virtues of plants, and better than the Ancients could by tasting them.[26]

Although we are mainly concerned here with vegetable works in alchemy, these principles apply to all three realms: animal, vegetable, and mineral. The spagyric process is subdivided into three main steps. The first step is separation of a material's essential components in the form of a crude spirit, soul, and body. These components are then purified using a variety of methods available to the laboratory worker. Finally the purified body soul and spirit are reunited into a new homogeneous matter free from corruptibility as a perfected form of the original substance. In short, the steps are labeled as separation, purification, and cohobation. An example will illustrate.

Most alchemical works, and this is true of the herbal works especially, begin with the process of putrefaction. It is only in death that things will give up their spiritual principles. This is known as philosophical death in the laboratory. In nature things will die and decay and their constituents will be dispersed back into nature. In the alchemist's laboratory the spiritual components are trapped in a vessel they can't escape from, sometimes referred to as a glass coffin, so the plant is allowed to die and ferment and in doing so it gives up the ghost, the volatile spiritual constituents. This process is one of reverting the vegetable material into its own vegetable chaos or Prima Materia. It is said that things will resolve themselves into that of which they were made; so this vegetable chaos represents the elements that were brought together under the action of the Substantial Form/Sulfur which resulted in the plant itself.

We take now this vegetable chaos and place it into a retort and gradually apply heat. The first thing that rises is a volatile spirit this is labeled as the alchemical Mercury and set aside. Now the heat is increased gradually and water will start to come over this is called

26   John Baptista Porta, *Natural Magic*, (1558), X, proem.

the flood or Phlegm. Soon the water will become colored and sour, smoke will arise followed by drops of thick dark oil. This combustible oil represents the alchemical sulfur in a crude state. What remains in our retort is a lump of black charcoal in which are hidden the pure mineral salts or the body of the plant.

We have now separated the three essential portions of the plant: its body, soul, and spirit. The next step of the spagyric process is that of purification. The volatile Mercury and thick black oil are re-distilled several times to purify and spiritualize them. The charcoal which remained at the bottom of the retort is placed into a hot fur-nace and calcined into a white ash which represents the true body of the plant. Once these three essential ingredients have been purified, all of their external hindrances, accidents and dysfunction have been removed. Now in a sort of resurrection the mineral salts, the body of the plant, are reunited with its purified Sulfur and Mercury to create what alchemist Isaac Holland called a Glorified Corpus, able to ex-press the plants true character without any hindrances or distortion. This process described above goes under the general term of spagyric anatomy which is discussed in great detail in the work, The Golden Chain of Homer. The process brings to mind the ancient Egyptian ritual of uniting the Ba and Ka of the deceased individual to become an Akhu or "Glorified One," able to commune through a prepared body and move between worlds unhindered.

In his commentary to the *Triumphal Chariot of Antimony* by Basil Valentine, Dr Theodor Kerkring comments on the activity of these medications and though he's speaking directly of antimony prepa-rations what he says also applies to these vegetable-based materials: "these medicaments do not work sensibly as emetics, cathartics and sudorifics are wont to do but, insensibly by uniting their own more purified universal spirit with our own spirit, amending Nature and re-storing Health."[27] Spagyric medicines are held to be "living medicines" and evolved representatives of the species they are derived from.

27 Theodor Kerkring, commentary to the 1678 *Triumphal Chariot of Antimony* by Basil Valentine.

When now the Spiritus and Corpus come together and are united after their preparation, one can do wonderful things with them, since they have then a hundred times more power than they had previously, for after the Conjunctio of the Souls and Body there exists a Glorified Corpus and a Great Elixir. With it one performs miracles.

—ISAAC HOLLAND (CIRCA 1480)

Book Ten of John Baptista Porta's twenty books on *Natural Magic* (1558) covers the art of distillation. In it he presents the following short insight to the use of distillation to determine the qualities of a plant.

How to Finde out the Vertues of Plants.

There are no surer searchers out of the Vertues of the Plants, then our Hands And Eyes; the Taste is more fallible: for, if in Distillation, the hottest parts evaporate first, we may conclude, that it consisteth of hot and thin parts: and so of the rest. You may easily know by the separation of the Elements, whether a Plant have more of Fire or Water, or Earth, by weighing the Plant first: then afterwards, when the Water and Oyl are extracted, weighing the Feces, and by their proportion you may judge of the degrees of each Element in the Composition of it, and from thence of their Qualities. But the narrow limits of this Book will not give me leave to expatiate farther on this Subject. Wherefore I will leave the Discourse of it to a particular treatise, which I intend to set out at large on the, matter.[28]

That pretty much hits the nail on the head for this study, from the distilled weights of the various collected fractions of a plant we may "judge of the degrees of each element in the composition of it and from thence of their qualities."

28   Baptista Porta, *Natural Magic*, X:179.

DISTILLATION OF PLANTS FROM THE
GOLDEN CHAIN OF HOMER (1723)

Grind, cut up, squash everything green as well as you can, and if it has not enough juice by its own nature, pour as much putrefied rainwater, or wine, or salt water upon it that it turns into a thin paste. Or, if you wish, press the juice out of it and let it ferment, like wine, or the way farmers make cider from pears or apples. Every soft and juicy plant can be treated this way, as can also the hard ones when they have been ground fine and a sufficient quantity of moisture has been added to them. Or, keep all the plants turned thus in a paste together. Put the paste in a lukewarm spot and let it thus soak until it gives off a sourish or foul smell—about fourteen days and nights, or three weeks. Then put it into an alembic and slowly distil the subtle volatile with its soft Phlegma. Remove what is left over, dry it completely and put it into a retort in sand and distil by degrees. In this way, you will first obtain a grosser Phlegma, then an Acid liquor, then the thick Oil; and then a lump, burnt to coal will stay at the bottom. Now the plant has been separated. You should note however, that as plants are not one like another, they are also unequal in regard to their component parts, for one has a great deal of volatile, the other more or oil, according to whether it has specified, coagulated and congealed much universal seed in itself. In accordance with these constituent parts, their virtues and powers are also likewise distributed and are to be assessed and then applied. For a fragrant plant, if it has much Volatile, that is, burning, has the power to strengthen and heal not only the natural vital or animal spirit but also the mentalem. If it has no pleasant fragrance, it invigorates the natural animal and vital spirit, although it does not always depend upon the outer noble fragrance but rather on the inner, through which, distilled by the Archeus, often quickly comforts and heals the wounded organ. If the plant contains a great deal of Acidum, it is specified to heal the tighter limbs, such as muscles, sinews, bones, cartilages, thicker and viscid vessels, etc. Likewise the Oil: the thicker the essential parts are, the thicker and more coagulated parts of the body they strengthen or destroy depending on how they are applied.

[...]

Likewise, the warm spirit of a plant or an animal warms a cold melancholicus, whereas a cold soporific or painkilling spirit cools a cholericus. This en passant. A physician knows anyhow how to cure the specific qualities.[29]

---

29   *Golden Chain of Homer*, Part 2, Ch. 8, 401.

SPAGYRIC ANATOMY OF PLANTS

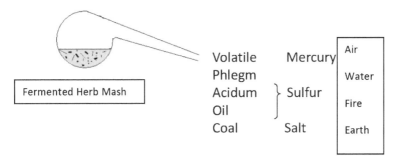

Volatile	Mercury	Air	
Phlegm		Water	
Acidum	} Sulfur	Fire	
Oil			
Coal	Salt	Earth	

Fermented Herb Mash

THE DRY DISTILLATION OF PLANTS

In his *Opus Vegetabilis*, Isaac Holland describes the process of distilling herbs that have been carefully dried. Holland calls the moisture of fresh plants, "Water of the Clouds," and describes it as locking up the elements in the plant fettering their ability to act; he thus also calls it the "Evil Cloud Water."

After you have drawn from the herbs the evil wateriness, keep them standing closed in the fire. Give them a slow and gentle fire for 12 hours, somewhat stronger every hour. Then there will go from them a white, red or yellow smoke, according to the spirit of the herbs. For there are some herbs that have a red spirit, but all ordinary herbs of the world have a white spirit.

With this gentle fire one gives it, increasing it gradually for twelve hours, the element air will in the meantime go over. That is the white, or the colored spirit.

When now the air, or the white spirit, has been drawn over cleanly in such a way, you must heat stronger for another 12 hours, increasing every four hours; still stronger for 20 hours; and as strong as you can during the last four hours, so that the barrel stands in the heat. The oil will go over within that time, mixed with the air, or whatever it is to be called. Then you have drawn the three elements from the earth. First, the water, then the air, and following that, the oil or fire.[30]

PREPARATION OF THE QUINTESSENCE   *HOLLAND CH. XVII*

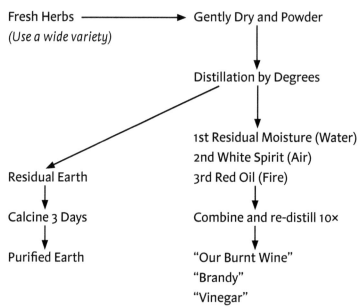

Fresh Herbs ————————▶ Gently Dry and Powder
(Use a wide variety)

Distillation by Degrees

1st Residual Moisture (Water)
2nd White Spirit (Air)
Residual Earth   3rd Red Oil (Fire)

Calcine 3 Days   Combine and re-distill 10×

Purified Earth   "Our Burnt Wine"
                        "Brandy"
                        "Vinegar"

30   Isaac Holland, *Opus Vegetabilis*, Ch. 17.

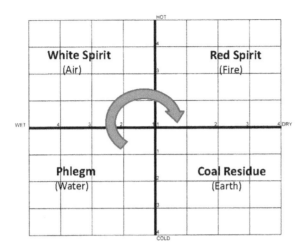

*The products from the dry distillation are obtained in
the same order as the seasons, beginning with winter
(associated with Phlegm) and ending with the coal
residue representing the Melancholic humor.*

Antoine Francois De Fourcroy (1755–1809) was a chemist during the
time when chemistry was undergoing great changes. The old ways
of Aristotle, Galen, and Avicenna were being called into question,
and the true nature of the elements was under scrutiny in numerous
laboratories across Europe. Although Fourcroy received his medical
degree from the Paris Faculty of Medicine in 1780, he never practiced; instead, his passion was for the science of chemistry. He succeeded P. J. Maquer as Chair of Chemistry at the Jardin du Roi and
became very popular for his lectures in chemistry and Natural History. Fourcroy also collaborated with some of the early proponents of
modern science, including Antoine Lavoisier and C. L. Berthellot, in
the revision of chemical nomenclature. The chemistry of animal life
was of great interest to Fourcroy and he investigated the various solid
and liquid substances of the body, applying the methods of laboratory chemistry to help improve medical understanding. Although,
by his time, the practice of dry distillation of materials to determine

their elemental constitution had largely fallen out of popularity, he gives a description of it that is clear and concise. Included here is the complete chapter on destructive distillation of plants by Antoine De Fourcroy in volume 4 of his *Elements of Natural History and Chemistry*, written in 1782:

CHAP. XVII.
Concerning the Analysis of Plants, by Destructive Distillation, on a naked Fire.

AFTER having examined all the substances which may be obtained from
plants, by simple methods, which are incapable of changing them; and after having
considered these matters as the immediate principles of organized substances, it is necessary to attend to the alterations they suffer when exposed to heat.

The ancient chemists were acquainted with no other method of analyzing vegetables, and all their researches into the nature of these bodies, consisted in determining how much spirit, oil, and volatile salt they afforded by distillation. This method is at present no longer esteemed, as it is known, that most plants afford nearly the same products; and the distillation of a great number of different vegetables, made by chemists, in other respects deserving the esteem of the public, has only served to undeceive us.

In fact, how can it be imagined, that the action of fire, exerted on all the different principles in a vegetable substance, such as extract, mucilage, oil, resin, salt, gluten, &c. which decomposes each of these principles in a peculiar manner, can afford any knowledge respecting their nature and quantity ; more especially when it is observed, that the products of these several decompositions unite together, and produce new substances, such as did not exist in the vegetable under examination ? The analysis of vegetables, by distillation, is therefore complex and fallacious.

However, as none of the methods which art is in possession of, ought to be neglected, in the chemical examination of any substance, we may have occasional recourse to this analysis, always carefully observing, that it is not too much to be depended on. It sometimes happens, that when the effects of aqueous, spiritus, and oily menstrua, on any substance, are compared with the alterations produced in it by fire, these last confirm the deductions made from the action of the solvents, and by the products of the distillation, indicate the substances contained in greater or less quantities, the nature of its salts, &c. But to make valuable deductions from the analysis by fire, it is necessary,

1.To be well acquainted with the action of fire, on each immediate or proximate principle, such as extract, mucilage, saline matter, oily juices, the fluid, or solid part, &c.

2. To compare the products, afforded by distillation, of the whole vegetable, with those usually afforded by the proximate principles, treated in the fame manner.

3. To analyze the vegetable by menstruums, in order to obtain its proximate principles, and to make useful inductions from the alterations it has sustained by fire.

The process of distilling vegetables by a naked fire, is very easy and simple. A given quantity, of a dry vegetable, is put into a glass, or earthen retort, so as to fill it not more than half or two thirds; the retort is then placed in a reverberatory furnace, and a receiver of a proper size adapted. It was formerly supposed necessary to use a receiver, perforated with a small hole, to give vent to the air said to be disengaged from vegetables, and tending to burst the vessels. But it is at present known, that the æriform fluid, which escapes from these bodies during distillation, is scarcely ever air, but consists of cretaceous acid and inflammable gas. Now, as these elastic fluids are products of the vegetable compound, by fire, as well as the phlegm, the oils, and the volatile salts, it is equally necessary to collect them. For this purpose, a perforated receiver, communicating with an inverted glass vessel, filled with water or mercury, may be used. By this means, the liquid products are collected in the receiver, and the æriform products under glass vessels, placed on the shelf of a pneumato-chemical apparatus. When the substance distilled affords a concrete salt, an adapter, or long glass vessel, is fixed between the retort and the receiver, in order that the sublimation may be made on its internal surface.

The operation is begun, by placing a few pieces of lighted charcoal beneath the retort, and the fire is gradually increased till the vessel is red-hot, and nothing more comes over.

After the whole has become cold, the apparatus is unluted, to examine each of the products obtained. Though the distillation of vegetables never affords products which may be considered as principles of the plant, yet these products differ considerably from each other, and require to be carefully distinguished.

The first product which comes over, is an aqueous liquor, containing certain odorous and saline principles. As the distillation advances, the colour and saline properties of this phlegm become stronger. It is succeeded by an oil, whose colour, consistence, and weight, gradually increase. From some vegetables, a light and fluid oil is obtained; but from others, a ponderous oil, capable of becoming concrete. The smell of this oil is always strong, and empyreumatic. During the time it comes over, a quantity of elastic fluid is disengaged, which consists either of the cretaceous acid, or inflammable gas, but most commonly of a mixture of both. At this period it is that the volatile alkali sublimes, when the vegetable is of such a nature as to afford it. When all these substances are past, the residue of the vegetable is of the nature of coal. We shall now proceed to examine more particularly into the nature and origin of each of these products.

The phlegm is produced from the water that enters into the composition of the vegetable, and partly from the water of vegetation, especially when the matter is not entirely dry; so that its quantity is greater or less on this account. The phlegm is coloured red, by a small quantity of oily matter which rises, and is usually rendered saponaceous, by the salt contained in the fluid. The saline matter is most commonly acid; for which reason the phlegm usually reddens syrup of violets, and causes an effervescence with cretaceous alkalis.

This acid arises from the mucilage, and the oil. But the phlegm is sometimes alkaline, as happens when nitrous or cruciferous plants, or emulsive and farinaceous feeds, are distilled; and it is often ammoniacal, because the volatile alkali succeeds the acid, and combines with it. This fact: may be ascertained by the addition of a small quantity of quicklime, or alkali, by which a strong smell of volatile alkali will be produced, when ammoniacal salt is present. Though the acids of vegetables do not appear to be all of the fame nature, those which are obtained, in their dissolution, exhibit the fame external characters but they have not yet been sufficiently examined to ascertain their properties with any degree of accuracy. The oils obtained from vegetables in this method, are all strong- smelling, highly-coloured, and possess nearly the fame properties. Those parts of vegetables which contain a large quantity of these inflammable fluids, such as the emulsive feeds, afford a large quantity of oil in their analysis. Odoriferous plants afford an oil, which, at the beginning, slightly partakes of their peculiar smell, but quickly assumes the characters of other oils of this kind, namely, colour, weight, and an empyreumatic smell. All these fluids are very inflammable; the nitrous acid sets them on fire, and they are soluble in spirit of wine.

They may all, by rectification, be rendered very fluid, light, and colourless, and be converted into the state of ethereal or essential oils. The volatile salt, or ammoniacal chalk, is only obtained from certain vegetables; but it is not true, as some chemists have affirmed, that it is afforded only by the cruciferous plants. All plants in general, which contain a certain quantity of glutinous or vegeto-animal matter, afford more or less of volatile alkali, by virtue of the mephitis, shewn by Mr. Berthollet to exist in this vegetable principle. It is very seldom, however, that any considerable quantity is obtained in the concrete state, as it is usually dissolved in the last portions of the phlegm. This salt is produced by the union of the mephitis with the inflammable gas of the oil, and for this reason it most commonly passes over towards the end of the distillation. It even seems, that the volatile alkali, which rises with the phlegm in the analysis of certain plants, such as the cruciferous plants, poppy, rue, &c. is always the product of a new combination; since Rouelle the younger has shewn, that the plants themselves do not contain it in their natural state.

The elastic fluids, disengaged during the distillation of vegetables, appear to depend on the nature of the vegetable. A plant, which contains a large quantity of oily combustible fluid, affords inflammable gas. Mucilages, on the contrary, afford cretaceous acid. We have observed, at the article of the acid of sugar, that Bergman and Fontana obtained a large quantity of cretaceous acid from that substance, and that the latter chemist thinks, that vegetable acids are for the most part composed of it. It is not, therefore, to be wondered, that mucilages, in which Bergman discovered the fame acid as exists in sugar, should afford cretaceous acid.

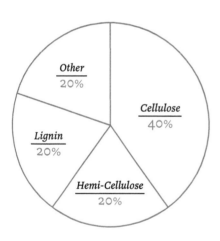

Lastly, there are some vegetable matters which afford atmospheric mephitis. These æriform fluids are not extracted till near the end of the distillation, when the vegetable becomes entirely decomposed. Hales, who was not acquainted with their nature, observed, that the quantity of air disengaged during the distillation of vegetables is greater, the more solid they are; whence he concluded, that this element was the cementing principle and cause of solidity in bodies. It is easy to form a proper opinion of this hypothesis, from what has been already said.[31]

---

31   Antoine De Fourcroy, *Elements of Natural History and Chemistry*, Vol. 4, (London, 1788).

MODES OF PYROLYSIS AND MAJOR PRODUCTS

Mode	Conditions	Liquid	Solid	Gas
Fast	*Very high heating rate to 500°C* *Short vapor residence <1sec*	75%	12% Char	13%
Intermediate	*Medium heating rate to 500°C* *Hot vapor residence 10–30 sec*	50%	25% Char	25%
Slow	*Slow heat to 500°C*	33%	33% Char	35%

GENERAL CHARACTER OF DISTILLATE

20–25%	Water
25–30%	Pyrolytic Lignin
5–12%	Organic Acids
10%	non-polar Hydrocarbons
5–10%	Anhydrosugars
10–25%	Other Oxygenated Compounds

pH 2–4 distinctive acrid, smoky odor

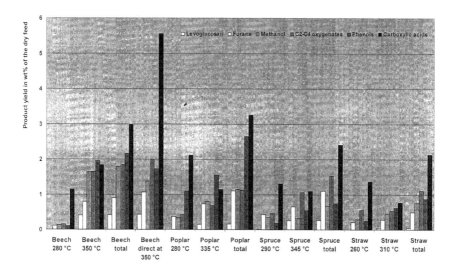

ΦΑΡΜΑΚΟ-ΒΑΣΑΝΟΣ:

OR, THE

Touch-ſtone of Medicines.

Diſcovering the

VERTUES

Of { VEGETABLES,
MINERALS, &
ANIMALS,

BY THEIR

TASTES & SMELLS.

In Two Columes.

By Sir *JOHN FLOYER*, of the City of *Litchfield*, Kᵗ. M. D. of *Queens-College*, Oxford.

Saporum Speculatio plurima jucunda, & non minùs utilia in ſe continet. Willis *de A-nima Brutorum.*

LONDON,

Printed for *Michael Johnſon*, Bookſeller in *Litch-field:* And are to be Sold by *Robert Clavel,* at the *Peacock* in St. *Paul's* Church-Yard. 1687.

Sir John Floyer (1649–1734) was a physician trained in Queen's College, Oxford and later set up practice in Lichfield. He was one of the most original thinkers of the period and an avid supporter of practical research. Floyer wrote a number of medical works including one on asthma and a hydrotherapy method using cold baths. His work on pulse measurement and development of the "Pulse Watch" reawakened interest in this neglected practice which has now become commonplace.

His first book titled, *Pharmaco-Basanos, or The Touchstone of Medicine*, is of interest in the present study. In it, Floyer describes a system for identifying medicinal qualities of plants and their relative degrees using taste as the main guide. We examined some of these ideas earlier with Galen and Avicenna. What is different and additional from Floyer's work is that he includes observations on the distillation of various herbs and reports them as watery, acidic, oily distillates and earthy residues very similar to Jabir's work on distilling materials to discover their mixture of elemental qualities. A few excerpts from this work will help clarify his ideas:

> If we use the testimony of our senses for the discovery of the Principles of ingredients, out of which the juices of plants, by different mixtures, are produced; they will inform us of Earthy, Watery, Oily, and Acid Principles; and a pungency which is a salt.
>
> I distilled some Gum-Arabic in an open fire, and in an earthen retort, and found an Acid spirit of a smokey smell, and a good quantity of Oil; but the Earthy parts exceeded all, Gum-Arabic being a clammy mucilage.
>
> Bitters yield a great deal of Oil by distillation, as wormwood, centaury, bitter almonds; olives have also a bitterness.
>
> That much earth concurs to the production of bitters, and fixing of turpentine, appears, in that all bitters produce much Salt, which we call Fixed, but the Oil in which the bitterness resides is easily driven away by the fire and remains not in the Salt or Earth; whence it is also proved to be an Oil, fixed by its crude associates, Acid and Earth.
>
> I Distilled half a pound of Gentian roots, in an earthen retort, in an open fire; from it was distilled an Acid liquor, with the Water, and a bitter Oil, without any volatile salt; which confirms my hypothesis, of bitterness being an Oil fixed by Acid: and the Caput Mortuum exceeded all the liquor in the receiver.

Galen makes four degrees of the virtues of plants, reducing them to Hot, Cold, Moist, and Dry.

That is Hot in the first degree, which does not evidently heat, but we find it by some reason about the Nature of it.
Those that manifestly heat, are of the second order.
Those which vehemently heat, are of the third order.
Those which burn, or induce eschar, are of the fourth degree.

But seeing the virtues of plants are so evidently deduced from their tastes, and those tastes so well experimented by many chymical distillations and mixtures; and since the Nature of the humors of the body, and all diseases, have been better observed than in Galen's time; I have not confined myself, in describing the Natures of plants to Hot, Cold, Dry and Moist; but have added all the compositions of tastes, and sensible effects of their modes; whereby I might particularly express the Nature of each plant: and according to the experimented virtues of tastes, I have added those which belong to each particular; and, I think, I need add no more, but the several degrees of taste; which may most easily be understood, and which may have a different degree of virtue. I therefore have observed three degrees in tastes: As for instance;

In bitters the first degree is a little bitter or bitterish; which does but just sensibly affect the taste; and therefore have the lowest degree of virtue, as bitter.

The second degree is bitter absolutely; which considerably affects the taste, and is of a moderate bitterness.

The third degree is very bitter; which much offends the taste, and has the highest degree of bitters.

The same degrees are observable in Acid, Sweet, Mucilaginous, Acrid, Aromatic, Watery, and Earthy Tastes.

Nature itself has prepared our medicines by mixtures, strainings, and digestions; and given to each plant a particular composition of tastes, and sometimes compounded odors, designedly suited and fitted for the particular vitiated humors in animals. For plants were not only designed for our nourishment, but likewise for our physick; and those that were for food, are found out by their pleasant sweet taste, and grateful odor; but those for medicine, by the offensive or nauseous taste and smell.

If we should torture our nourishment by the same degrees of fire as medicines are prepared, we should destroy that natural sweetness of our food; which is a fitter taste for aliments than those of Spirits, Oils, Salts, Tinctures, etc. So it happens in medicines, when we distill Oils, ferment the juices into Spirits, and make Tinctures, we make new Mixtures, and destroy the natural tastes and virtues of vegetables.

If from aromatic plants, as wormwood or mint, we distill an Oil; that will have the bitterness and acrimony of the plant but will want the astringency of it; and besides the empyreuma, which makes it very burning inwardly, the Oily Salt is more burning and Hot than our humors, spirits and membranes can endure; therefore when it is thus prepared, we find it necessary to remix it with gritty powders and take them in a cool vehicle. These distilled Oils are not therefore much used, unless for outward applications.[32]

Floyer derived much of his inspiration from the earlier work of Nehemiah Grew, whom he mentions on several occasions with great respect. Nehemiah Grew was born in England in 1641, graduated from Cambridge University in 1661 and received his medical degree from the University of Leiden in 1671. While carrying on an active medical practice throughout his life, Grew was also active in medical research. At the time, there existed a great body of information on the anatomy of animals and of man but very little of the same for plants. Recognizing the need, Grew undertook detailed microscopic examination of vegetable life. He published a number of essays covering the

---

32   John Floyer, *Pharmako-Basanos or The Touch-stone of Medicines.* Vol.1 (London, 1687).

anatomy roots, leaves, flowers, fruits and seeds; many of which were read before the Royal Society. The culmination of these researches was published in his great work, *The Anatomy of Plants* illustrated with 82 detailed plates and having appended seven papers of a chemical nature. For the present study, several of these appended papers are of great interest because they present a detailed scheme linking taste to medicinal qualities and to products obtained by distillation of the plant. His appended Lecture VI,[33] titled, "A Discourse of the Diversities and Causes of Tastes Chiefly in Plants," was read before the Royal Society on March 25, 1675, presenting a detailed examination of taste and its use in determining the nature and density of a plant. The diagram below is an overview of Grew's classification of taste wherein he divides taste into the nature of the sensation itself and into the nature of its effect in the subject.

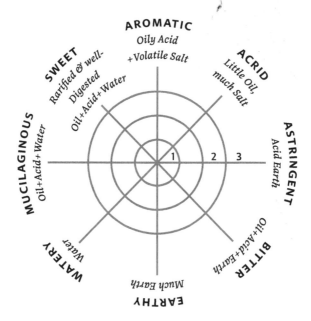

Floyer's observations on taste and products from the destructive distillation of plants in each taste category.

---

33   Nehemiah Grew, *The Anatomy of Plants* (London: The Royal Society, 1682), 279.

Grew subdivides the sensation into simple tastes, of which he lists fifteen, and compound tastes, of which he describes only six; beyond that, language fails as there are no terms which describe the many possible combinations. Grew calculates that just combining two simple tastes into a compound taste produce 45 combinations and compounding three simple tastes will produce 120 different taste sensations. There are still more nuances of taste because in addition to the taste there is an associated degree of intensity (*gradus*) from mild to overpowering. In general, Grew allows five degrees of intensity for each "Species" of taste, but also mentions that some are capable of ten degrees of detectable difference. So, by Grew's calculation, combining simple tastes by threes and factoring in the intensities on a scale of five degrees will produce 1800 "sensible and definable variations" of taste. How these tastes affect the sensory apparatus of the subject is the second aspect to taste that Grew subdivides into Duration and in Respectu subjecti, that is, in respect to the various taste sensing receptacles of the person tasting the drug. Duration of taste, describes the timing of sensation from first contact and sense activation, through an increase of sensation to a maximum followed by a period of sustained maximum intensity. After this, the taste subsides over a varying span of time called the "Declinatio." With respect to the subject, tastes can be Fixed, meaning the sensation keeps within the compass of one part for the full duration; or the taste can be Diffusive, meaning it slowly spreads without leaving its point of origin. Finally the taste can also be Transitive, meaning it wholly quits the point of origin and is transferred to another part.

Classification of taste by Nehemiah Grew, The Anatomy of Plants 1675

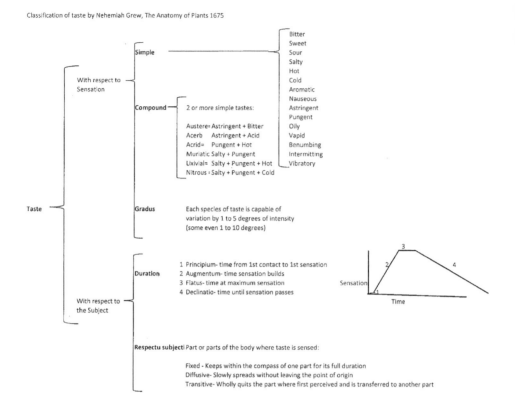

Some of the taste intensities assigned to herbs by Nehemiah Grew in discussing his system of Gradus in tastes:

HERB	TASTE INTENSITY
Turmeric	Bitter 1st Degree
Roses	Bitter 2nd Degree
Gentian	Bitter 10th Degree
Hellebore Root	Bitter 2nd Degree, Hot 3rd Degree
Yarrow	Bitter 4th Degree, Hot 1st Degree
Calamus Root	Bitter 4th Degree, Hot 1st Degree, Aromatic 3rd Degree

In chapter four of his discourse on taste, "Of the Causes of Taste," Grew says, "But the immediate causes, besides the organs of taste, are the Principles of plants. As many of which, as come under the notice of the sense, we have already supposed to be these seven, Alkaline, Acid, Air, Water, Oil, Spirit, Earth."[34] These are the products from distillation of the plant material. Water is of course the Phlegmatic humor, Acid, Air, and Spirit are encompassed by the Sanguine fraction, Oil representing the Bile while the Melancholic humor, the ash, provides the Alkaline and Earth Principles. Grew connects tastes to the dominance of one or more of these Principles, so for example, if we taste an astringent plant we would expect to find an abundance of Acid and Earth in the distillation products from that plant.

TASTE	DOMINANT PRINCIPLES
Unctuous	Oil
Vapid	Water or Earth
Pungent	Alkali or Sharpened Acid
Penetrant	Salt soured or guarded by Earth
Sour	Acid soiled with Earth
Salt	Acid guarded by Alkali and soiled with Earth
Cold	Acid drowned in Water and soiled with Earth
Hot	Oil or Sulphur
Sweet	Alkali or Acid smoothed by Sulphur or by both Spirit and Sulphur
Bitter	Sulphur well impregnated with an alkali or Acid salt with some Earth
Astringency	Acid with Earth
Aromatic	Spiritous, Acid, and Volatile Sulphur

Another interesting work appended to *The Anatomy of Plants* was titled "An Essay of the Various Proportions Wherein the Lixivial Salt is Found in Plants." This paper, read before the Royal Society in March of 1676, contains some of Grew's observations on salts obtained from calcined plants. He calls them lixivial salts meaning they are salts ob-

---

34   *Ibid.*, "Of the Causes of Taste."

tained by first burning a plant to ashes, a process called calcination, followed by mixing the ash with water and filtering. The insoluble portion remaining in the filter is called the Earth of the plant; the water solution that was filtered off is dried to reveal an alkaline salt, this is the alkali of the plant and held to be its Essential Salt. Grew approaches the project with a series of queries such as; do wood and barks produce more salt than leaves and flowers? Or, how do the various proportions of Salt to Earth follow taste?

> It is the part of the Physician, knowingly and artificially to use and govern Nature. And therefore by every likely Method, to inspect the state and properties of all sorts of bodies. One Method, is that I have taken in the foregoing Experiments, that is, by mixing them with several Menstruums or Liquors: whereby we may be assisted to judge, both the Kinds and the Proportions of Principles in any Body; and of the manner of their mixture in the same.
>
> Another is by Calcining them; or, as it were, by mixing them with the Fire, a potent and almost universal Menstruum. I shall here only set down some trials for an essay upon plants; chiefly noting, the different Proportions of their Lixivial Salts.[35]

ANALYSIS OF LIXIVIATED SALTS FROM CALCINED HERBS

Herb	Amount of Lixiviated Salt	Equivalent in grams
Ash Bark	32 grains	2.08
Rosemary	5 scruples	6.48
Agrimony	5 scruples, 6 grains	6.87
Mint	½ ounce, ½ dram	17.49
Oak Bark	½ dram	1.94
Licorice	½ dram	1.94
Anise Seed	2 scruples	2.59

35   *Ibid.*, Essay on Lixivial Salts, Lect. III, Ch. 1, 255.

Herb	Amount of Lixiviated Salt	Equivalent in grams
Sorrel	1 dram	3.88
Mugwort	2 drams, 2 scruples	10.35
Senna	4 ½ scruples	5.83
Flax Seed	50 grains	3.25
Rhubarb	1920 grains	124.8

Grew also noted that some plants gave a quantity of *caput mortuum* or "Dead Head," meaning the Calcined ashes, but there were little to no salts produced by the lixiviation process only the Earth remained. The issue of how to deal with the Salts obtained in the distillation process is a long standing problem as there are volatile salts that distill over with the oil, sometimes in large quantities and they are difficult to separate from the oil. Do they count as part of the Oil or as part of the Earth? And for the Earth itself do we count only the lixiviated salts, the Earth, or both? The answer could have an important influence in the final calculation of intensity. This same issue will come up later in the practical section of this study and may even factor in to future investigations. Along the same line is the question of fresh versus dried plant materials used in the distillation. Is there a "Standard of Dryness" that won't bias the quantity of Phlegm obtained? Some very interesting data is already available on the distillation of fresh plants in the work of Etienne Francois Geoffroy.

Etienne Francois Geoffroy (1672–1731) was a French chemist who began his career in medicine as an apothecary studying at Montpellier. He went on to become Professor of Chemistry and Pharmacy at the College Royal in 1709. Geoffroy's lectures on *materia medica* were published as a series of volumes titled, *Traite de la Matiere Medicale* in 1741, and contain details on the "Chymical Analysis" of dozens of medicinal herbs. He provides both qualitative and quantitative observations of the products obtained by destructive distillation of mainly fresh plant materials recording the nature and amount of each as phlegm, acid, oil, volatile salts, coal, fixed ash, and lixiviated salts.

Dans l'Analyſe Chymique de ℔v. de feuilles de Piſſenlit fleuries, diſtillées à la cornue, il eſt ſorti ℔j. ℥iv. ʒv. gr. lx. de liqueur limpide, preſque ſans odeur, inſipide, d'abord obſcurément ſalée, enſuite obſcurément acide : ℔ij. ℥xiv. ʒij. gr. xviij. de liqueur d'abord limpide, manifeſtement acide, enſuite rouſſeatre, un peu auſtère : ℥ij. ʒv. gr. xij. de liqueur rouſſe, empyreumatique, d'abord obſcurément acide, un peu ſalée, auſtère, & enfin imprégnée de beaucoup de ſel volatil-urineux : ℥j. ʒij. gr. xxiv. d'huile fluide.

La maſſe noire qui eſt reſtée dans la cornue, peſoit ℥vij. laquelle étant bien calcinée, a laiſſé ℥iij. ʒvij. de cendres rouſſeatres, dont on a tiré par la lixiviation ʒiij. gr. xxxvj. de ſel fixe ſalé, un peu alkali. La perte des parties dans la diſtillation a été de ℥ij. gr. xxx. & dans la calcination de ℥iij. ʒj.

Example analysis for 5 lbs fresh leaves of dandelion from Geoffroy's Traite de la Matiere Medicale, *1741.*

As a future part of this study, I have selected sixty of Geoffroy's analy-
ses for translation and conversion of his apothecary weights to grams.
The final weight percents of products from the original sample distilled will be compared with the products from distilling the dried
plants, and in some cases the fresh material will be distilled to compare with Geoffroy's results.

FINIS

Part Two: Practice

SCOPE OF RESEARCH

T HE original scope of this research was to determine whether or not instrumental thermogravimetric analysis (TGA) could mimic the alchemist's separation of elements by distillation. This would allow data collection on a wide variety of plant materials easily for comparison of their physically measured humors with their traditional temperament. For example, Avicenna lists garlic as Hot in the third degree and Dry in the second degree; do the humors as determined by TGA support this designation?

Fifty plants were chosen for the study initially, but the number has nearly doubled. Many of the herbs used grow locally or were cultivated in my garden so that I would have better control over how and when a plant was harvested, as well as how it was dried and prepared for analysis. One criterion for plant selection was the availability of traditional designations of elemental intensities from two or more sources, Avicenna's *Canon of Medicine* and *Culpeper's Herbal* being preferred.

As the following narrative will explain, the original method using TGA revealed some enticing patterns but several problems arose, and the TGA methods were supplemented with the traditional method of high temperature dry distillation.

In addition to this work on the so-called "simples" of the *materia medica*, several compound medicines were prepared in order to compare their experimental result with the predicted value according to traditional calculations from the formula.

METHODOLOGY
THERMOGRAVIMETRIC ANALYSIS
OF PLANT MATERIALS

Thermogravimetry studies the change of a sample mass as a function of temperature. The measurements of these changes are made using a thermobalance in which tests are accomplished according to a programmed heating rate in a suitable enclosed system with a controlled atmosphere. For this study, a TA Instruments 2950 Thermogravimetric Analyzer was used with ultrapure nitrogen as a cover gas to prevent oxidation and so more closely resemble the conditions inside a distillation flask or retort. Dried samples of powdered herb were heated at a rate of 20° Celsius per minute from room temperature (20°C) to 600°C. Given the small sample size of 20 to 50 mg this rate was selected to mimic "distillation by degree" within a convenient time span allowing for multiple sample runs.

Author photo.

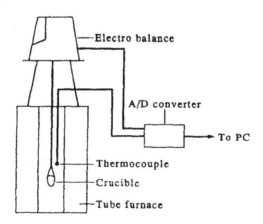

I ran several herb samples for proof of concept and could easily see that each gave a similar response but each was also different, like a fingerprint. The similarity was that each of the herbs revealed three main areas of weight loss and a residual lump of "coal." These areas correspond to the fractions distilled out of the herb as described in the alchemical works above. First, the watery Phlegm distilled out up to about 200°C, followed by the colored acidic fraction as the Air element or Sanguine humor from 200° to 400°C, finally the dark combustible oil distills out as the Fire or Choleric humor from 400° to 600°C. The residue remaining in the distillation flask, or in our case, the TGA sample pan, represents the "calx" or Melancholic humor (it is even black and caustic like black bile).

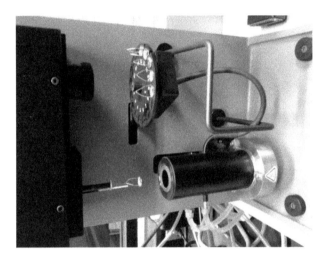

Author photos.

I was concerned with the reproducibility of the analysis so a sample was run twice, days apart, then compared and showed very good correlation. This was repeated on additional plant samples revealing not only good reproducibility between individual samples, but also characteristic patterns in the thermogram like a fingerprint.

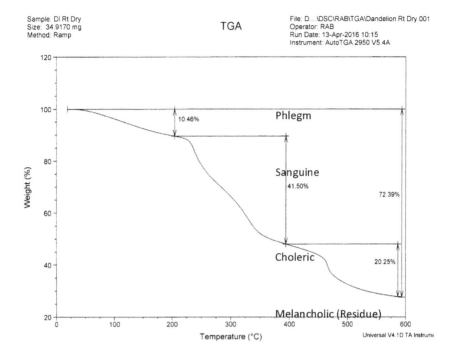

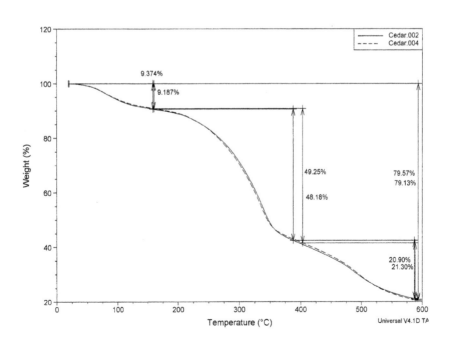

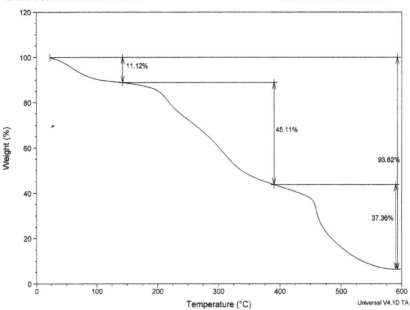

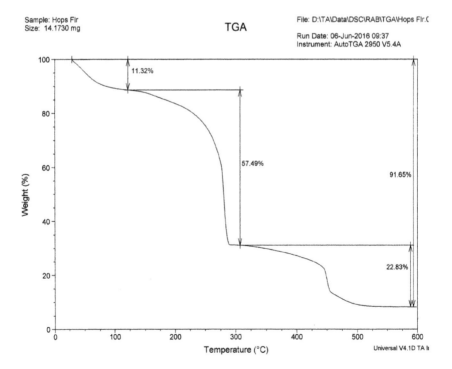

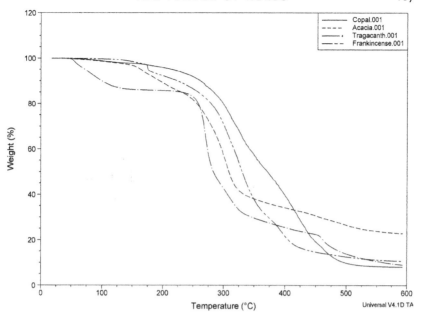

*Comparison of similar gums and resins reveals
characteristic curve shapes like a fingerprint.*

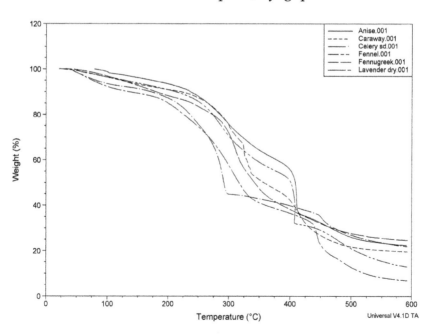

Comparison of some common herbs.

I wondered if individuals of a species would produce the same results. A sample of Red Cedar growing outside my house was gathered and then samples from two other Red Cedars were collected. One of these trees was two miles away and the other was twenty miles away. The results also indicated good correlation and maintenance of the characteristic curve shape.

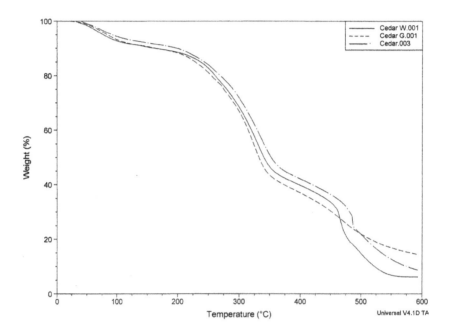

The data I was collecting seemed to be reproducible from herb to herb and between individuals of a species widely separated in the environment. Even herbs harvested years apart retained their characteristic shape except for some flattening due to loss of volatiles over time. I was satisfied that the method had some potential, so I began collecting TGA data for as wide a variety of plants as were available. Many of the herbs were collected locally from the Pacific Northwest forests or grown in my own garden so I could ensure their freshness and drying treatment. All of the wild-crafted herbs were dried in the shade until they were easily powdered by rubbing between the hands as suggested by Isaac Holland. Naturally there were a large number of more exotic spices that were examined as well; these were generally good quality certified organic sources selected from various herb suppliers locally.

CALCULATION OF INTENSITY

Once the TGA run was complete, the resulting graph of temperature versus weight loss was subjected to analysis by software that would allow placement of markers to calculate the weight lost in the three sections of interest. In general, the Phlegm passed over by 200°C, followed by the Sanguine humor passing over between 200° and 400°C. Finally the Choleric humor or dark oil passes over from about 400° to 600°C. The coal-like residue that remained was calculated as the Melancholic humor. The humors are physical representatives of the Four Elements which in turn represent two of the Elemental Qualities, so the calculated weight percent values were divided by two and the resulting half values placed into their respective column on a table as shown below.

DRIED DANDELION Root

Fraction	Element	Wt %	Hot	Cold	Wet	Dry
Phlegm	Water	10,5		* 5,2	* 5,2	
White Spirit	Air	41,5	* 20.8		* 20.8	
Red Spirit	Fire	20	* 10			* 10
Residue	Earth	28		* 14		* 14
Sub-Total		100				
Final Result			30.8 19,2		26 24	
			11.6 Hot		2 wet	

Next, the totals for the each of the four qualities were obtained by adding the column values. Values for the active elements, Hot and Cold, were added algebraically to obtain the dominant quality. The same process was repeated for the two passive qualities, Wet and Dry. In this way the dominant qualities and their relative intensity for the material were obtained.

All of the data gathered from the various plants in this way were then placed into a larger table to see if any pattern or trend could be determined. By examining the ranges of the elemental qualities by column, it was found that the average high value was around 32; which was convenient because it allowed a simple division by 8 to arrive at a relative degree of intensity. So, the final balances between Hot/Cold and Wet/Dry were divided by 8 to obtain a degree designation like Hot in the third degree and Wet in the first degree, which is given in shorthand as H3W1. A value between 1 and 8 is in the first degree, from 8 to 16 is in the second degree, 16 to 24 the third degree, and 24 to 32 the fourth degree. As an example let's say our final totals were 11 Hot and 19 Dry. That would be Hot in the second degree and Dry in the third degree, abbreviated herein as H2D3. This was just a first try at assigning an intensity to the

SUMMARY TABLE OF TGA RESULTS

Plant	Scientific Name	Phlegm	Sanguine	Choleric	Melancholic	Hot	Cold	Wet	Dry	Final Balance	TGA Result	Canon II	Culpeper	Gerard	Salmon	Pirate	Markham
Acacia	Acacia nilotica	8	56	13	23	35	16	32	18	19H 14W	H3W2	C2D2					
Alder	Alnus viridis	9	42	14	36	28	23	26	25	5H 1W	H1W1		C2W2			H2D2	H3D3
Anise	Pimpinella anisum	5	30	42	22	36	14	18	32	22H 14D	H3D2	H2D3	H2D2	H3D3	H2D1		
Avens	Geum macrophyllum																
Basil, Garden	Ocimum basilicum											H2D1	H3W3	H2W1	H1D1		
Bay Lvs	Laurus nobilis	16	44	23	16	34	16	30	20	18H 11W	H3W2	H3D2	H3D3	HD	H2W2		HD
Birch Lvs	Betula alba	9	49	13	29	31	19	29	21	12H 8W	H2W1		C2W2			H3D3	
Black Pepper	Piper nigrum	7	55	15	23	35	15	31	19	20H 12W	H3W2	H4D4			C1D1		H4D4
Burdock rt	Arctium lappa												H1D1	HD			
Caraway	Carum carvi	9	42	30	19	36	14	26	25	22H 1W	H3W1	H2D2	H3D3	H3D3	H3D3	H3D3	H3D3
Cardamom	Eletaria cardamomun											H3D3					H

Common name	Latin name								TGA values obtained			Traditional values (various sources)
Celery sd	Apium graveolens	8	48	23	21	36	15	28	22	21H6W	H3W1	H3D3
Chickweed	Stellaria media	18	40	30	12	35	15	29	21	20H8W	H3W1	
Cinnamon	Cinnamomun zeylanicum	8	55	16	21	36	15	32	19	21H13W	H3W2	H3D3 H3D3
Cleavers	Galium aparine	19	41	29	11	35	20	30	25	15H5W	H2W1	H3D3 C1D1 H1D1 H2D2 H3D3 c
Cloves	Eugenia caryophyllata	12	40	25	23	32	18	26	24	14H2W	H2W1	H3D3 C3D3 C1D1 CM
Comfrey	Symphytum officinale	2	43	47	8	45	5	23	28	40H5D	H4D1	
Copal	Protium copal	6	38	30	26	34	16	22	28	18H6D	H3D1	C2D2 C2D2 HD
Coriander	Coriandrum sativum	8	37	30	25	34	17	23	28	17H5D	H3D1	H2D3 C1D1 C1D1 H3D3 H3D3 H3D3 H3D2
Cumin	Cuminum cyminum	10	43	20	28	31	19	26	24	12H2W	H2W1	H3D2 C2D2 C1D1
Dandelion	Taraxacum officinale	10	40	25	25	33	23	30	25	10H5W	H2W1	H1D1 H3D2 H2D2 H3D3 H3D3 H2D2 CW
Dill	Anethum graveolens	9	32	21	18	37	14	31	20	23H11W	H3W2	H3D2 H1D3 C2D3 HC=D2 H2D2 H3D2
Dock	Rumex crispus	9	36	42	13	39	11	28	28	28H5D	H4D1	H2D1 H3D3 H3D3 H3D3 H3D3 H3D3
Fennel	Foeniculum vulgare	13	30	33	24	47	19	22	44	28H22D	H4D3	H1D1 H2D1 H2D1 H2D1 H2D2 H2D2
Fenugreek	Trigonella foenum-graecum	8	61	20	11	41	9	35	16	31H19W	H4W3	H4D4 H4D4 H4D4 H4W3 H3D3
Frankincense	Boswellia carteri	11	33	28	28	31	25	27	28	6H1D	H1D1	H4D4 H4D4 H4D4 H4D4 H
Garlic	Allium sativum	16	43	19	22	32	19	30	21	13H9W	H2W2	H3D2 H4D3 H3D3 H3D3 C2D2
Ginger	Zingiber officinale	11	62	18	9	40	10	36	14	30H22W	H4W3	H3D3 H3D3 H3D3
Hawthorn	Crataegus oxycantha	11	58	23	8	41	10	35	16	31H19W	H4W3	H2D2 H2D2 H3D3 C2D2
Hops	Humulus lupulus	8	38	24	30	31	9	23	27	12H4D	H2D1	C1D2 H3D3 D HC=D3 HC=D3 H1D2
Horsetail	Equisetum arvense	12	49	30	9	40	11	31	20	29H11W	H4W7	H3D3 H3D3 H3D3 H3D3 H2D1
Lavender	Lavandula officinalis	11	45	37	6	41	9	28	22	33H6W	H4W1	H2D2 H2D2 H2D2 H2D2 H2D1
Melissa	Melissa officinalis	15	45	34	7	39	11	30	21	28H9W	H4W2	H1D2 H1D2 H2D2 H2D2 H2D3
Mugwort	Artemisia vulgaris	10	58	20	12	39	11	34	16	28H22W	H4W3	H3D3 H1D1 H2D2 HC=D1 H2D2 H2D2
Mullein	Verbascum thapsus	6	37	18	39	28	22	21	29	6H8D	H1D1	H2D2 H1D1 D HC=D1 H2D2 HD
Myrrh	Commiphora myrrha	10	42	33	15	37	13	26	24	24H2W	H3W1	H3 H2D2 H1D2 H1D1 H1D2 H2D2
Nettles	Urtic dioica	14	41	21	25	31	19	27	23	11H5W	H2W1	H4D4 H4D4 H2D2 H4D4
Onion	Allium cepa	8	46	15	31	31	20	77	23	11H4W	H2W1	C2D2 H3D2 H4D2 H2D2 H1D2
Parsley	Petroselinum	9	45	26	20	36	15	77	23	21H4W	H3W1	C3W2 C2D2 C3W2 C1D1 C1D1 C3D3
Plantain	Plantago major	11	34	22	33	28	22	23	28	6H5D	H1D1	CD
Purslane	Portulaca oleracea	3	54	36	7	45	5	29	21	40H7W	H4W1	
Red Clover	Trifolium pratense	26	39	32	3	36	15	33	18	22H16W	H3W2	C1 C1W1 C1D2 C2D3 C2D3
Rose	Rosa damascena	9	49	13	29	31	19	29	21	12H8W	H2W1	H3D3 H2D2 H3D3 H2D2
Rosemary	Rosmarinus officinalis	9	45	25	21	35	16	77	24	19H3W	H3W1	H2D1 H3D1 H2D1 H2D2 H2D2 H2D1 H2D1
Saffron	Crocus sativum	10	43	29	18	36	14	77	24	22H3W	H3W1	H3D3 H3D3 H3D3 H3D2 H3D2 H2D2
Sage	Salvia officinalis	4	79	2	15	41	10	42	9	31H33W	H4W4	H1W1
Sesame sd	Sesamun indicum	8	46	36	10	41	9	77	23	32H4W	H4W2	C3D3 CD/HD HC=D2
Shepherds purse	Capsella bursa-pastoris	15	36	24	25	30	20	26	25	10H1W	H2W1	H2D2 H2D2 HD H1D1 H1D2
St. Johnswort	Hypericum perforatum	27	42	26	21	44	16	27	34	28H7D	H4D1	H3D3 H2D3 H3D3 H3D3 H3D3
Thyme	Thymus vulgaris	10	42	30	17	36	14	26	24	22H3W	H3W1	H2D2 H2D2
Tobacco	Nicotiana tabacum	14	57	20	9	39	12	36	15	27H21W	H4W3	H1W1
Tragacanth	Astragalus gummifer	11	57	19	13	38	12	34	16	26H18W	H4W3	
Turmeric	Curcuma longa	6	27	22	45	25	26	17	34	1C17D	C1D3	H2D2 H C1D2 H2D2 H2D1 H2D2 H1D2 H H3D1 H3D3
Valerian	Valeriana officinalis	8	51	25	16	38	12	30	21	26H9W	H4W2	H H1D2 C2D2 H1D1 C2D2
Willow	Salix alba	7	51	20	22	36	15	29	21	21H2W	H3W1	H1D2 H1D1 C2D2 H3D3 H3D3
Wormwood	Artemisia absinthium	12	48	24	16	36	14	30	20	22H10W	H3W2	C1W1 C1D2 CD C1D1 C1D1 H1D2

resulting values and it seemed to provide close approximations, many of which, if not exactly according to its traditional value were within a degree or two, which variation we see in the classical designations themselves.

DERIVATIVE THERMOGRAVIMETRY

Using more advanced analysis software, I was able to obtain the derivative of the thermogram. This secondary curve of the plot indicates how quickly the sample weight is changing. Determining where to take measurements of the fractions as they boiled off became much easier and precise.

*   *

*

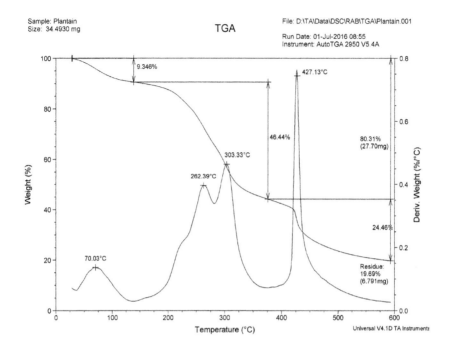

Sample: Plantain
Size: 34.4930 mg

TGA

File: D:\TA\Data\DSC\RAB\TGA\Plantain.001
Run Date: 01-Jul-2016 08:55
Instrument: AutoTGA 2950 V5.4A

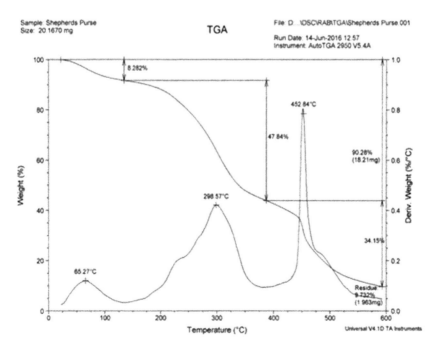

Sample: Shepherds Purse
Size: 20.1670 mg

TGA

File: D:\...\DSC\RAB\TGA\Shepherds Purse.001
Run Date: 14-Jun-2016 12:57
Instrument: AutoTGA 2950 V5.4A

Analysis by DTGA

Material	Phlegm	Sanguine	Choleric	Melancholic	Hot	Cold	Wet	Dry	Final Balance	Result 8/Deg
Birch lvs	9	49	13	29	31	19	29	21	12H 8W	H2W1
Caraway sd	10	32	35	23	34	17	21	29	17H 8D	H3D1
Cinnamon	8	55	16	21	36	15	32	19	21H 13W	H3W2
Comfrey rt	14	38	18	30	28	22	26	24	6H 2W	H1W1
Coriander sd	7	57	15	21	36	14	32	18	22H 14W	H3W2
Fennel sd	7	32	37	24	35	16	20	31	19H 11D	H3D2
Ginger rt	10	52	12	26	32	18	31	19	14H 12W	H2W2
Hawthorn brs	11	62	18	9	40	10	36	14	30H 22W	H4W3
Melissa lvs	10	48	10	32	29	21	29	21	8H 8W	H1W1
Plantain lvs	9	45	26	20	36	15	27	23	21H 4W	H3W1
Thyme lvs	11	50	10	29	30	20	31	20	10H 11W	H2W2
Turmeric rt	12	52	8	28	30	20	32	18	10H 14W	H2W2
Willow bk	12	52	19	17	36	15	32	18	21H 14W	H3W2
Wormwood lvs	7	51	20	22	36	15	29	21	21H 8W	H3W1

JABIR'S DESIGNATION OF FRACTIONS

The TGA results seemed heavily biased towards Hot and Wet designations; a thought occurred that Jabir assigned the fractions from the distillation differently than Holland or The Golden Chain of Homer. Jabir labeled the Oil fraction as Air and the 'Tincture' or aqueous fraction he called the Fire. The Phlegm was still the watery fraction and the residue was still called Earth, he just switches around the Air and Fire designations so that the Oil represents the Sanguine and the acid liquid that follows the Phlegm represents the Bile. Visually, this makes sense as the Oil looks like blood, the Sanguine; and the Acidum looks like Bile. This change in the calculation of temper would mainly affect the Wet/Dry ratio.

Most of the traditional listings of herb temperament show a preponderance of Hot and Dry qualities. In the study by Ramezany et al in 2013, 339 plants from 29 families were statistically analyzed using Old Persian pharmacopeia designations of primary qualities. As can be seen in the following two graphs from that work, a large proportion of the medicinal herbs are of a Hot and Dry nature.

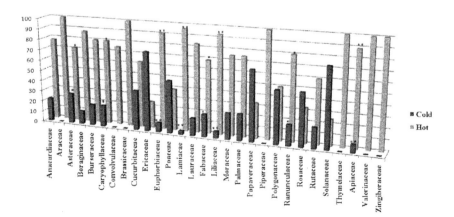

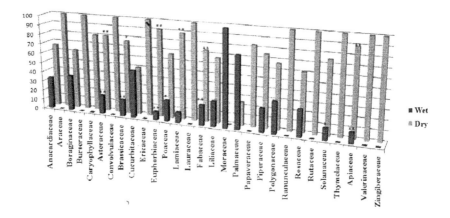

I decided to re-calculate the DTGA data using Jabir's designation of fractions and it had the predicted effect of increasing the Dry quality of the final result as can be seen in the table below.

PROBLEMS WITH THE TGA METHOD

Calculation of temper using Jabir's designation of fractions came a little closer to the mark, however, in the end it was just shifting around a deeper problem. During the distillations a certain amount of non-condensable gasses are released; this is mainly carbon dioxide, carbon monoxide, and methane. These non-condensable gasses were counted as weight loss in the TGA sanguine fraction thus biasing results towards Hot/Wet (sanguine is Hot and Wet).

In a study on the pyrolysis of wood by DeGroot et al., the onset of this gas release was measured to be around 250°C and gas release continued to about 400°C, which is exactly the range where the Acid Liquor distills over. The graphs below show the onset, peak, and ending of the gas released from wood samples. The lignin and cellulosic materials in our herbs under test would follow a similar release pattern to the woods tested by DeGroot. This is also the temperature range in the TGA which shows the largest weight loss, some of which

Analysis by DTGA/Jabir

Material	Phlegm	Sanguine	Choleric	Melancholic	Hot	Cold	Wet	Dry	Final Balance	Result
		Oil	Tincture							8/Deg
Birch lvs	9	13	49	24	31	17	11	37	15H 26D	H2D4
Caraway sd	10	35	32	23	33	17	23	28	17H 5D	H3D1
Cinnamon	12	38	46	4	42	8	25	25	34H W/D=	H4W/D=
Comfrey rt	14	18	38	30	28	22	16	34	6H 18D	H1D3
Coriander sd	7	16	57	20	36	14	11	39	22H 27D	H3D4
Fennel sd	7	37	32	24	34	16	22	28	18H 6D	H3D2
Ginger rt	10	29	54	7	42	9	20	31	33H 11D	H4D2
Hawthorn brs	11	18	62	9	40	10	15	36	20H 21D	H3D3
Melissa lvs	10	10	48	32	29	21	10	40	8H 30D	H2D4
Plantain lvs	9	26	45	20	36	15	13	33	21H 15D	H3D2
Thyme lvs	11	10	50	4	30	8	11	27	22H 17D	H3D3
Turmeric rt	12	8	52	28	30	20	10	40	10H 30D	H2D4
Willow bk	12	19	52	17	35	15	15	35	20H 20D	H3D3
Wormwood lvs	7	20	51	22	36	14	13	37	21H 23D	H3D3

is liquid distillate representing the sanguine humor and some is from non-condensable gasses. Of course we could capture and condense these gasses with modern technology but they would not have been part of the weighing of distillation fractions by the ancient workers. Antoine DeFourcroy, as mentioned above, at least made attempts to capture and measure these gasses with a pneumatic trough. He describes the event as a "disengagement of Elastic Fluid" containing "cretaceous acid" (wet CO2) and a "mephitic fluid" (foul smelling and flammable vapors).

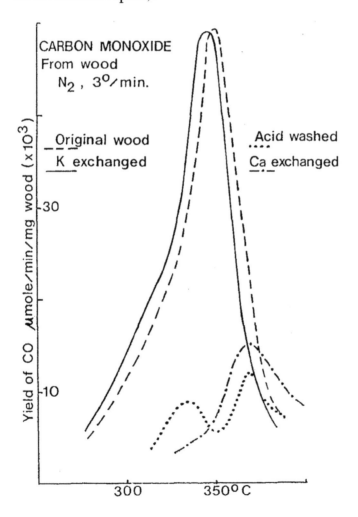

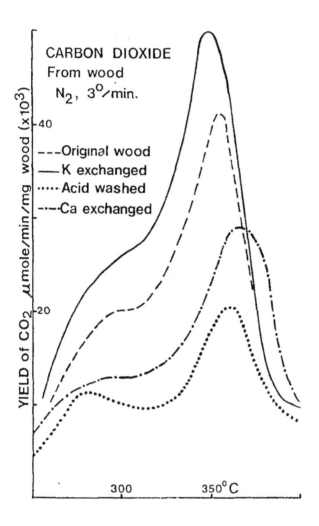

I'm sure the ancient distillers ran into the gas release problem in the form of bursting vessels and wonder if it had any bearing on designating this second fraction following the Phlegm as the Air element. Nicholas Lemery in his *Course of Chymistry* written in 1698 mentions the problem in his description of distilling guaiacum wood.[36] The section is reproduced here as it provides another good description of

36 Nicholas Lemery, *Course of Chymistry* (1698), Part 2, Ch. 3, 475.

the operation and events observable in distilling the herbs and also includes the weights of the fractions obtained.

DISTILLATION OF GUAIACUM

This operation is a separation of the liquid parts of Guaiacum, from its terrestrious matter.

Take the shavings of Guaiacum, fill a large retort with them three quarters full, place it in a reverberatory furnace, and join to it a great capacious receiver. Begin distillation with a fire of the first degree, to warm the retort gently, and to distill the water, which is called Phlegm; continue it in this condition, until there come no more drops, which is a sign that all the Phlegm is distilled. Throw away that which you find in the receiver, and fitting it again to the neck of the retort, lute well the junctures. You must afterwards increase the heat by degrees, and the Spirits, and Oil will come forth in white clouds; continue the fire until there comes no more, let the vessels cool, and unlute them, pour that which is in the receiver into a funnel lined with brown paper, set upon a bottle, or some other vessel, the Spirit will pass through and leave the black, thick, and very fetid Oil in the funnel; pour it into a vial and keep it for use; it is an excellent remedy for the rottenness of bones, and for the tooth-ache, and to clean old ulcers. It may be rectified as I said of the Oil of Amber, and may be used inwardly in the epilepsie, palsie, and to drive forth the afterbirth: the Dose is from two drops to six. The Spirit of guaiacum may be rectified by distilling it by an alembic, for to separate a little impurity that might have passed with it; it works by perspiration, and by urine: the Dose is from half a dram to a dram and a half, It is likewise used mixed with the water of honey, to cleanse inveterate ulcers.

You will find in the retort the coals of Guaiacum, which you may turn into ashes by putting fire to them, which they will sooner take than other coals: Calcine these ashes some hours in a potters furnace, then make a lixivium of them with water, which being filtered, evaporate it in a glass or earthen vessel in sand; there will remain the Salt of Guaiacum, which you may make white by calcining it in a crucible in a strong fire. This Salt is aperitive, and sudorific; it may serve as all other alkalis to draw the Tincture of Vegetables: the Dose is from ten grains to half a dram in some convenient liquor. The Earth, called Caput Mortuum, is good for nothing.

After this manner the five substances of all vegetables may be drawn; but because the fire doth give them a loathsome Empyreumatical smell, other ways have been invented to draw the Oil of aromatics: I shall describe them in the sequel.

Remarks

During the distillation of Spirits, you must not make the fire too strong, for they coming forth with a great deal of violence, would else be apt to break either the retort or the receiver.

Though the Guaiacum that is used be a very dry body, yet abundance of liquor is drawn from it; for if you put into the retort four pounds of this wood, at sixteen ounces to the pound, you'll draw nine and thirty ounces of Spirit and Phlegm, and five ounces and a half of Oil; there will remain in the retort nineteen ounces of coals, from which you may draw half an ounce or six drams of an Alkali salt.[37]

ANALYSIS BY FIRE

Although the TGA analysis was not panning out entirely, the results were still very enticing—especially when considering the various known method and equipment errors—enough to consider it worthy of further investigation. Since the loss of non-condensable gases

37   *Ibid.*

skewed the results toward Hot/Wet designations, a change of methodology was planned which took us back to the alchemical roots of elemental analysis.

The new method of analysis involved high temperature dry distillation of weighed samples of herb powder, as described by Isaac Holland and The Golden Chain of Homer. In this way, the actual fractions obtained could be weighed and determination of intensity would follow as in the TGA analysis.

Above and facing: Images from Antidotarium Geminum *of Weckero, 1595.*

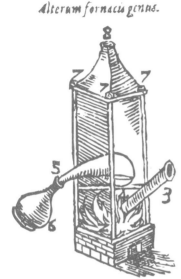

Alterum fornaciu genus.

1 *Porta, per quam aer ingrediens ignem fouet.*
2 *Craticula, cui carbones incumbunt.*
3 *Piger Henricus, carbones deferens.*
4 *Locus quo repositum est oblongum ferrum sustinens boccam.*
5 *Collum boccae prominens, deorsum inclinatum.*
6 *Recipiens magnum.*
7 *Ventilia quatuor.*
8 *Foramen magnum in summitate fornacis.*

The following protocol was adopted for the initial investigation of the distillation method:

Fire Analysis Procedure

Place approximately 10 grams of powdered herb into the 25ml round-bottom distilling flask and attach the 90° elbow distilling head.

Place about ¼ inch of sand into the electric crucible and place the thermocouple on top of it. Insert the distilling flask and fill in around it with sand.

Attach the condensing arm and pear-shaped 50 ml receiver.

Begin heating slowly to about 150°C. The clear "Phlegm" should begin distilling.

Maintain the temperature at 150° to 200°C maximum for about one hour. All of the phlegm will pass over and distillation will slow or stop.

Increase the heat and watch the distilling head carefully for the first sign of definite golden color. (Note: the phlegm may have a slight tint to it but the golden liquid that follows is definitely seen to be colored.)

When color first appears in the distilling head, quickly collect the phlegm into a pre-weighed vial. Replace the receiver and turn up the heat. Weigh the vial and calculate %Phlegm based on sample weight.

Allow the temperature to gradually rise to 600°C. The golden distillate and a dark heavy oil will co-distill and then separate in the receiver. (Oil on top, golden distillate at the bottom). Full run time is about 2.5 to 3 hours from the start up.

Turn off the heat when it is clear that nothing more will come over and let cool.

Detach the distilling flask and turn the condensing section to allow drainage into the receiver. Allow this to stand undisturbed for some time then remove the deep golden liquid from the bottom using a syringe. Place the liquid into a pre-weighed vial. Weigh the vial and calculate the % Sanguine.

Replace the condensing section onto the receiver, still containing the oil, and using a minimum of acetone, rinse all of the oil adhering to the glassware down into the receiver.

Using a syringe, transfer the acetone solution of oil into a pre-weighed watchglass and allow the acetone to evaporate leaving a viscous, deep amber oil (the Bile). Obtain the final weight of the oil and calculate the % Bilious.

Weigh the distilling flask containing the residue of black charred herb (the Black Bile). Obtain the residue weight and calculate the % Melancholic.

Heating was controlled with an electric crucible filled with sand.

Analysis by Fire

Date:

Sample ID: _____

Still Pot Tare Wt.   _____

Flask + Sample Wt.   _____   Type K
                                                    Time   **Mv**
Sample Wt.   _____

    Phlegm Tare: _____

    Vial + Phlegm: _____

    Wt Phlegm _____
    _____ %

    Sanguine Tare _____

    Vial + Sang _____

    Wt. Sanguine _____
    _____ %

    Bile Tare   _____

    Vile + Bile _____

    Wt. Bile   _____
    _____ %

    Melancholic Tare _____

    Vial + Melan _____

    Wt. Melancholic _____
    _____ %

Fraction	Element	Wt %	Hot	Cold	Wet	Dry
Phlegm	Water			*	*	
White Spiri	Air		*		*	
Red Spirit	Fire		*			*
Residue	Earth			*		*

Sub-Total   _____

Final Result   _____ _____   _____ _____

Distillation set-up and Data collection Sheet.

Collection of fractions after cooling.

The Sanguine and Choleric humors from coriander seed forming two layers in the receiver.

As mentioned by DeFourcroy and Floyer, quoted above, some plants produced a considerable amount of volatile salt, which was caught up in the oil and stuck to the inner condensing surface. Since it was so integrated with the oil, it was counted as a part of it.

The Four Humors distilled from coriander.

The Melancholic humor or Black Bile is the coal residue, or *calx*, from the distillation. In the center is the Fire element or Choleric humor as a dark combustible oil; next, to the right is the Sanguine humor, followed by the Phlegmatic humor on the far right. Visually, it looks as though the Choleric humor predominates, and that would make sense since coriander is listed as being Hot and Dry and it is a Mars ruled herb (Mars is a Choleric planet). However as Jabir pointed out long ago only the balance will tell since the Black Bile (Cold and Dry) will temper the Hot and Dry Choleric humor to some degree based on their relative weights.

If we use Jabir's designation of fractions, the dark blood-like oil would represent the Sanguine humor and the golden "Tincture," as Jabir calls it, would represent the bilious humor or Fire element, which as can be seen makes sense visually, and thus as the ancient workers would have witnessed from their distillations.

A number of herbs had to be distilled in this way to make an assessment of the results. Herbs were selected from the traditional lists of "simples" having a wide variety of temperaments. The initial trials were very encouraging.

CALCULATIONS OF INTENSITY

The weights of the collected fractions were converted to weight percent of the original powdered sample. Then, as with the TGA, each fraction's weight percent was divided by two, because the elements they represent are composed of two primary qualities. The resulting values were then placed according to the element.

Phlegm, the Water element, is composed of Cold and Dry qualities; so half its weight value goes to the Cold column and half goes to the Wet column.

The same follows for the other fractions, the Sanguine, Air element, is Hot and Wet; Choleric is Hot and Dry, while the Melancholic humor represented by the residual coal, carries the Cold and Dry qualities.

The values were placed into a table and the total for each quality was obtained. The values for the active elements Hot and Cold were added algebraically to obtain a dominant Hot or Cold final balance.

The same process was applied to the passive elements Wet and Dry. All of the data collected from the several distillations was then placed into a larger table for comparison.

In the analysis by TGA, the final balances of the qualities were divided by 8 to arrive at an intensity designation; here it was found convenient to divide by 4 to arrive at the degree of intensity. This made the results match closely to their traditional values.

Analysis by Fire rev.1

Material	Phlegm	Sanguine	Choleric	Melancholic	Hot	Cold	Wet	Dry	Final Balance	Result 4 per deg	Notes
											Canon II
Birch lvs	17	13	20	30	17	24	15	25	7C 10D	C2D3	C2W2
Caraway sd	15	14	29	23	23	20	14	29	3H 15D	H1D4	H2D2
Cinnamon bk	11	20	28	32	24	22	16	30	2H 14D	H1D4	H3D3
Comfrey rt	15	20	3	38	12	27	17	21	15C 4D	C4D2	C3D3
Coriander sd	10	17	24	26	21	18	13	25	3H 12D	H1D3	C2D2
Fennel sd	7	16	18	26	17	16	11	22	1H 11D	H1D3	H2D1
Ginger rt	8	33	11	24	22	16	21	17	6H 4W	H2W1	H3D2
Hawthorn brs	14	29	22	27	26	21	22	25	5H 3D	H2D1	H3D3
Melissa lvs	14	21	16	28	18	21	17	22	3C 5D	C1D2	H2D2
Plantain lvs	13	17	14	31	15	22	15	23	7C 8D	C2D2	C2D2
Thyme lvs	13	18	21	28	20	20	15	24	1C 9D	C1D3	H3D3
Turmeric rt	12	25	14	27	20	20	19	21	H/C= 2D	H/C=D1	H2D2
Willow bk	17	20	8	36	14	26	18	22	12C 4D	C2D2	C2D2
Wormwood lvs	10	23	18	28	21	19	17	23	2H 7D	H1D2	H1D2

Analysis by Fire REV.1/Jabir

Material	Phlegm	Sanguine	Choleric	Melancholic	Hot	Cold	Wet	Dry	Final Balance	Result 4/DEG
Birch lvs	17	20	13	30	17	24	19	22	7C 3D	C2D1
Caraway sd	15	29	14	23	22	19	22	19	3H 3W	H1W1
Cinnamon	11	28	20	32	24	22	20	26	2H 6D	H1D2
Comfrey rt	15	3	20	38	12	27	9	29	15C 20D	C3D3
Coriander sd	10	24	17	26	21	18	17	22	3H 5D	H1D2
Fennel sd	7	18	16	26	17	16	13	21	1H 8D	H1D2
Ginger rt	8	11	33	24	22	16	10	29	6H 19D	H2D3
Hawthorn brs	14	22	29	27	26	20	17	28	6H 11D	H2D2
Melissa lvs	14	16	21	28	19	21	15	25	2C 10D	C1D2
Plantain lvs	13	14	17	31	16	22	14	24	6C 10D	C2D2
Thyme lvs	13	21	18	28	21	20	17	23	1H6D	H1D2
Turmeric rt	12	14	25	27	20	20	13	26	0H/C 13D	H/C=D3
Willow bk	17	8	20	36	14	27	13	28	14C 15D	C2D2
Wormwood lvs	10	18	23	28	21	19	14	26	2H 12D	H1D2

PROBLEMS ENCOUNTERED WITH THE
DISTILLATION

As the distillations continued, certain problems became apparent. Each distillation required about three hours to complete and needed close supervision for the first hour or so to collect the Phlegm at the proper time. Sometimes the proper time was not easy to distinguish, so accurate separation of the fractions became difficult, thus the Phlegm always had a little of the Sanguine in it and the Sanguine always had a little of the oil in it. Then there was the constant problem from hang-up of distillate in the glassware throwing the weights off a little.

That said, the distilled weights of Phlegm and Bile were reasonably close to those obtained by TGA; the problem was accurately determining the Sanguine humor weight. Another change of methodology was required, this time combining the distillation method with TGA.

The TGA results indicated the water or Phlegm distilling out first very clearly. The total distillate collected from the actual distillation separated naturally into an oily top layer and an aqueous layer at the bottom. This allowed direct weighing of the oil or Bilious humor. To determine the Sanguine humor, the sample weight of the herb was multiplied by the TGA % Phlegm to obtain the weight of Phlegm and this weight was then subtracted from the total collected weight of the aqueous layer; the result being the weight of Sanguine humor.

Distillation Procedure rev2

Record weight of distilling flask.
Add powdered sample and record weight of flask with sample.
Weigh entire condensing train plus pear shaped receiver.
Bury distillation flask in sandbath with thermocouple.

Attach condensing train and receiver.

Attach bubbler to receiver.

Turn heat to low.

Adjust heat as needed to maintain rate of about 3° or 4° per minute to 600° C,

Collect total distillate.

Turn off heat and let cool.

Weigh entire condensing train and receiver with distillate. Calculate Total Distillate as step 11 weight minus step 3 weight.

Set receiver upright, let stand overnight and allow the two layers to separate.

Using a syringe, remove the bottom layer from the receiver into a pre-weighed vial and obtain the weight as Phlegm and Sanguine combined.

Collect the oil into a pre-weighed vial and obtain the weight as the Choleric humor.

Weight of step 13 plus step 14 should equal the Total Distillate of step 11.

Weigh the distillation flask and calculate the residue weight as the melancholic humor.

Analysis by Fire rev 2

Material	Phlegm	Sanguine	Choleric	Melanchol	Hot	Cold	Wet	Dry	Final Balance	Result 4/DEG	Notes Canon II
Birch lvs	9	21	20	30	21	20	15	25	1H 10D	H1D3	C2W2
Caraway sd	10	19	29	23	24	16	14	26	8H 12D	H2D3	H2D2
Cinnamon	12	23	9	4	16	8	18	7	8H 11D	H2D3	H3D3
Comfrey rt	11	29	6	31	18	21	21	19	3C 2W	C1W1	C3D3
Coriander sd	7	24	24	46	24	27	16	35	3C 19D	C1D4	C2D2
Fennel sd	7	16	18	24	17	16	18	24	1H 9D	H1D3	H2D1
Ginger rt	10	13	29	7	21	9	12	18	12H 6D	H3D2	H3D2
Hawthorn bl	11	33	22	27	28	19	22	25	9H 3D	H3D1	H3D3
Melissa lvs	10	25	16	28	20	19	17	22	1H 5D	H1D2	H2D2
Plantain lvs	9	20	14	31	17	20	15	23	3C 8D	C1D2	C2D2
Thyme lvs	11	20	21	28	20	19	15	24	1H 9D	H1D3	H3D3
Turmeric rt	12	25	14	27	20	20	19	21	0H/C 2D	H/C=D1	H2D2
Willow bk	12	25	8	36	17	24	18	22	7C 4D	C2D1	C2D2
Wormwood	7	27	18	28	22	18	17	23	4H 6D	H1D2	H1D2

Analysis by Fire rev 2/ Jabir

Material	Phlegm	Sanguine (oil)	Choleric (tincture)	Melanchol	Hot	Cold	Wet	Dry	Final Balan	Result (4/DEG)	Notes (Canon II)
Birch lvs	9	20	21	30	21	20	15	26	1H 11D	H1D3	C2W2
Caraway sd	10	29	19	23	24	16	20	21	8H 1D	H2D1	H2D2
Cinnamon	12	9	23	4	16	8	11	14	8H 3D	H2D1	H3D3
Comfrey rt	11	6	29	31	18	21	8	30	3C 22D	C1D4	C3D3
Coriander sd	7	24	24	46	24	27	16	35	3C 19D	C1D4	C2D2
Fennel sd	7	18	16	24	17	16	13	20	1H 7D	H1D2	H2D1
Ginger rt	10	29	13	7	21	9	20	10	12H 10W	H3W3	H3D2
Hawthorn brs	11	22	33	27	28	19	17	30	9H 13D	H3D4	H3D3
Melissa lvs	10	8	25	28	16	20	10	27	4C 17D	C1D4	H2D2
Plantain lvs	9	14	19	31	17	20	12	26	3C 14D	C1D4	C2D2
Thyme lvs	11	21	19	28	20	19	16	24	1H 8D	H1D2	H3D3
Turmeric rt	12	14	25	27	20	19	13	26	1H 13D	H1D4	H2D2
Willow bk	12	8	25	36	17	24	10	30	7C 20D	C2D4	C2D2
Wormwood lvs	7	18	27	28	22	18	12	27	4H 15D	H1D4	H1D2

COMPOUND MEDICINES

A S discussed above, Galen advocated measuring the relative heating or cooling, drying or moistening action of a medicinal substance according to a scale of four degrees, based on the effects observed in the patient. Later Islamic physicians, the heirs of Galen, fine-tuned this scale by also measuring dryness and moisture, and subdividing the degrees into beginning, middle, and end of each degree. Medieval European physicians adopted this Arabic-Galenic system in the eleventh century, and it formed the basis of scholastic pharmacy for centuries to come. The system of degrees works easily if the physician prescribes only "simples," single ingredients, but how is the physician supposed to measure the qualitative strengths of a compound medicine, a drug made up of two or more herbs, or even dozens for that matter? This problem has vexed scholars for centuries and was the center of great debate in the medical schools of Salerno and Montpellier.

We can list a few reasons as to why compound herbal preparations are so attractive;

1. The strength and acuteness of the illness may be such that no single herb is sufficient against it.

2. Some very powerful and useful plants also possess toxic or poisonous side-effects in themselves which can be mitigated by combination with plants that nullify the toxic effect completely or inhibit the bioavailability of the toxin to an acceptable level. For example, tannins will bind with heavy metals and also with alkaloids and thus inhibit their absorption, so a plant rich in tannins could be used to control their effects.

3. The affected organ may be far from the site of administration, so herbs can be added which will direct the medicinal qualities of the main therapeutic herb to the desired organ or system.

4. Herbs may be added to extend the activity of the main therapeutic herb.

5. Herbs may be added to improve the palatability of the compound.

6. Prevention of harmful effects from an herb, such as the addition of peppermint to senna to prevent cramping.

7. It is believed that a multiplicity of factors and complications cause diseases in most cases, leading to both visible and invisible symptoms. The combination of herbs may act on multiple targets simultaneously to bring about rapid relief.

8. The overall complexity of the compound herbal is generally such that much smaller doses are required compared to single herb preparations.

Over the centuries, Western herbalists have developed certain guidelines for compounding effective herbal medicines, and these ideas stretch back as far as recorded history. In traditional formulations of the West, five or six herbs to a blend is considered an effective number providing all of the medicinal actions required and yet doesn't confuse the body with too many chemical combinations at once. Typically a formulation may contain two or three parts of the main therapeutic herb. This is an herb which is specific for the treatment of the particular condition. These are the "simples" applied to specific illnesses. To this is added one part of a soothing and relaxing herb for the affected area or to the nerves in general. Next, one part of a nourishing, strengthening, or tonic herb for the affected organ or system and finally, one part eliminative, alterative, or depurative to aid waste removal.

The human body is seen as a self-correcting mechanism; all we have to do is supply the correct temperament materials, insure their effective and unhindered circulation, and keep the channels of elimination open to affect a cure.

AL-KINDI

Al-Kindi (801–873) was an Arab philosopher and physician, from Baghdad. His quantification of medical theory influenced later medieval European pharmacy.

Medicine.	Pondera.	Caliditat.	Frigiditat.	Siccitat.	Humiditatis.
Mafticis	vn.ii.	ptes quator	pars vna.	ptes qtuor	pars vna.
Achori	vn.j.	partes due	pars femis	ptes due	pars femis.
Balauftie	vn.j.	ps femis.	ptes due	ptes due	pars femis
Darmel.	vn.i.	ptes qttuor	ps femis.	ptes qttuor.	pars femis.
Emblici.	vn.ij	ptes octo	pars vna.	ptes octo	pars vna.
Nigelle	vn.ii.	partes octo.	pars vna.	ptes octo	pars vna.
Eufozbii.	vn.i.	partes octo	pars femis	ptes octo	pars femis
Nafturtii.	vn.i.	partes octo	pars femis.	ptes octo	pars femis.
Mellis	vn.c.	partes.cc.	pars vna.	ptes.cc.	partes .l.

*Part of Al-Kindi's calculation process involved listing ingredients,
weights and their contribution of parts Hot, Cold, Wet, and Dry
based on individual temperaments of the simples.*[38]

Michael McVaugh, in several of his publications, has traced the solutions to the problem of how to quantify the actions of new, more complex drugs to masters in the universities of Montpellier and Bologna. These physician-professors, led by Arnald of Villanova, master in residence at the medical school of Montpellier between 1290 and 1300, applied more complex quantification to their pharmacology to predict the resulting final degrees of a compound medicine and to determine the final effect of varying weights of a drug. Arnald's solutions derived from reading in Latin translation the Arabic Islamic philosophers, al-Kindi and Averroës (ibn Rushd, 1126–1198). Al-Kindi, in particular, advised a geometric progression to the four degrees, which could then be applied to the calculation of intensities in a compound medicine.

---

38 *Alchindus, De Gradibus Medicinarum Compositaru*, attributed to Arnald De Villanova (1234–1310).

A simple drug with no discernible action was called "temperate" and calculated at a ratio of 1:1 (equally hot and cold). A drug that is hot in the first degree has a ratio of 2:1 (twice as much hot as cold), while the second, third, and fourth degrees increase geometrically (4:1, 8:1, 16:1). The same system of ratios also applied to dryness and moisture, but was not considered as important as heat. To give a simple example, if a physician compounded a drug out of two herbs, one hot in the second degree (4:1) and another cold in the first degree (1:2), then the ratios are added to determine the final quality of the drug. The sum ratio of 5:3 represents a gentle drug that can heat a patient just below the first degree (calculated at 2:1).

INGREDIENT	TEMPER	PARTS HOT	PARTS COLD
Drug #1	H2	4	1
Drug #2	C1	1	2
	Totals	5	3

WALTER OF ODINGTON

Walter of Odington was a monk at Evesham, having associations with Oxford and active around 1300 CE. He wrote on mathematics, geometry, music, chronology and astronomy. His work of interest to us here is titled *Icocedron*, a Greek name referring to its division into twenty chapters. The fifteenth chapter stresses the necessity of knowing the virtues of things in terms of degrees of the elemental qualities. Walter lists the intensity of the four elements as follows:

ELEMENT	INTENSITY
Fire	Hot in the 4th degree and Dry in the 3rd degree
Air	Wet in the 4th and Hot in the 3rd
Water	Cold in the 4th and Wet in the 3rd
Earth	Dry in the 4th and Cold in the 3rd

Chapter fifteen also includes proportions of the elements for many metals, minerals, and spirits.

In his monumental work, *A History of Magic and Experimental Science*, Lynn Thorndike gives a summary of Walter's method of calculating the intensities required of materials in a compound medicine, which can be tempered or balanced as desired:

> In the sixteenth chapter Walter gives instructions how to obtain the first qualities in a pure state by combinations of the elements in certain proportions, and how to obtain an incorruptible essence from mixture of the elements. For example, reckoning sixty minutes to the degree, Fire which is Hot in the fourth degree and Dry in the end of the third degree is reckoned to have 240 minutes of heat and 180 of dryness, whereas Earth, which is Dry in the fourth degree and Cold in the middle of the third degree will have 240 minutes of dryness and only 150 minutes of Cold. The idea is that by combining or counteracting a certain number of minutes of Fire with a certain number of minutes of Earth, one can either make Fire as Dry as it is Hot or can destroy the heat and cold and obtain pure dryness which is common to both elements.[39]

His work of isolating the first qualities (Hot, Cold, Wet, Dry) in a pure state and of obtaining "an incorruptible essence" is reminiscent of the work done by Jabir ibn Hayyan for creation of his transmutational "Elixirs."

39 Lynn Thorndike, *A History of Magic and Experimental Science*, 8 Vols. (New York: Columbia University Press, 1923-1958), III:131.

— Calculation of Elemental Qualities in Compound Medicines —

Calcul des différentes parts de qualités contraires dans les 4 degrès				
	Qualités actives			
	Qualité dominante : chaleur		Qualité dominante : froid	
	Parts de chaleur	Parts de froid	Parts de froid	Parts de chaleur
Degré 1	2	1	2	1
Degré 2	4	1	4	1
Degré 3	8	1	8	1
Degré 4	16	1	16	1

DEGREES BASED ON GEOMETRIC PROGRESSION OF DOUBLING, WHICH NATURE LIKES TO DO

Nombre de parts de chaque qualité dans un médicament équilibré				
Degré tempéré	Qualités actives		Qualités passives	
	Chaud	Froid	Sec	Humide
Nombre de part	1	1	1	1

"Temperate"

On peut, pour le contrôler, établir les rapports suivants :

	Méd. tempéré	Méd. testé	Méd. du 1er degré
Parts de chaud	1	32	2
Parts de froid	1	22	1

Ratio almost 1:1

example

Soit en réduisant au même dénominateur :

	Méd. tempéré	Méd. testé	Méd. du 1er degré
Parts de chaud	22	32	44
Parts de froid	22	22	22

Le médicament testé dépasse en chaleur de 32 – 22, soit 10 parties, la chaleur du degré tempéré. Il le dépasse donc en chaleur de 10/22es.

History
- *JABIR / Science of the Balance*   *1st 2nd 3rd 4th*
- *AL-KINDI – applies Mathematics & Pythagorean ideas → Degree Ratios 1:1 1:2 1:4 1:8 1:16*
- *IBN BIKLARISH – Book Al-Musta'ini Formulates Equations To Calculate Qualities in Compound Meds.*
- *ARNOLD DE VILLANOVA – perpetuates and expands Methods*

Example with weights factored in

	Simples	Poids (en dirham)	Parts de chaud	Parts de froid	Parts de sec	Parts d'humide
Temper						
C4D4	Opium	1	1	16	16	1
H3D3	Cannelle	4	32	4	32	4
H3D3	Aloès	2	16	2	16	2
H3D3	Asaret	2	16	2	16	2
H3D2	Costus	4	16	4	32	4
H2D3	Mastic	4	16	4	32	4
C1D2	Rose	4	4	8	16	4
H1D1	Nard	4	8	4	8	4
H1D1	Safran	4	8	4	8	4
	Total		117	48	176	29

(1 dirham = 4g)

L'analyse des résultats de ce tableau montre que le médicament composé est chaud et sec. Pour estimer son degré de chaleur, nous pouvons raisonner de la façon suivante :

	Méd. 1ᵉʳ degré	Méd. testé	Méd. du 2ᵉ degré
Parts de chaud	2	117	4
	----	----	----
Parts de froid	1	48	1

Si nous réduisons au même dénominateur :

Parts de chaud	96	117	192
	----	----	----
Parts de froid	48	48	48

Le médicament testé, comprenant 117 parts de chaud pour 48 parts de froid, se trouve situé, comme nous pouvons le vérifier à l'aide des rapports ci-dessus, entre le premier et le deuxième degré de chaleur. Il excède le premier degré de 117 – 96, soit 21 parties. Il le dépasse donc en proportion de 21/96ᵉˢ. Il est donc environ à un degré et 2/10ᵉ de chaleur.

Ce même composé est plus sec qu'humide. De la même façon, nous avons établi que le médicament dépasse en sécheresse le deuxième degré de 15/29ᵉ parties. Il est donc environ au milieu du deuxième degré.

The parts of a medicine taken dry[113]	weight in drams	nature	hot parts	cold parts	moist parts	dry parts
Scammony	7.5	3h/d	60	7.5	7.5	60
White pepper	4.5	4h/d	70	4.5	4.5	70
Cardamom[114]	4.5	3h/d	36	4.5	4.5	36
Ginger	1.5	3h/d	12	1.5	1.5	12
Cinnamon	1.5	3h/d	12	1.5	1.5	12
Mace	1.5	2h/d	6	1.5	1.5	6
Clove	1.5	3h/d	12	1.5	1.5	12
Nutmeg[115]	1.5	2h/d	6	1.5	1.5	6
Emblic myrobalan	1.5	1c/d	1.5	3	1.5	3
White sugar[116]	50	1h/d	100	50	100	50
Honey	105	2h/d	420	105	105	420
Total		end of 2h/mid-1d	735	182	230	687

SUMMARY OF RESULTS

I Call this PHASE ONE of the investigation, presenting some of the background and initial trials on proof of concept. There are still some issues to work out and make improvements to such as apparatus and weighing methods, but these first steps were very revealing. There are also the concerns over when and where a plant is harvested and even a particular growing season may have its consequences on the final distilled products. We also mentioned earlier there were problems with the salt, always a pivotal point in alchemy. Should the char, lixiviated salt, *caput mortuum*, or a combination be weighed as the Melancholic humor?

Hopefully PHASE TWO will help to clarify some of these issues and provide new insights into the viability of the method to provide a reliable classification of a material's temperament. Still, I wanted to get this much of the puzzle out there in case there were other interested parties who would like to pursue the idea as well.

In PHASE TWO, several compound medicines will also be examined. These will be selected from early pharmacopoeias which provide a precise temperament for the remedy and not just 'heating' or 'cooling'. This will be an interesting test of the method as well as a test of the methods used to calculate what the mixture should be as advocated by Al-Kindi and Arnold De Villanova.

FUTURE WORK

Continue building database

·

Seasons and astrological timing

·

Planetary rulerships

·

Improved experimental setup: conditioning chamber, oven dry for phlegm wt

BIBLIOGRAPHY

Adamson, Melitta Weiss. *Food in Medieval Times*. Westport, CT: Greenwood Press, 2004.

Aegineta, Paulus. *The Seven Books of Paulus Aegineta*. Translated by Francis Adams. London: Sydenham Society, 1847.

Ahsan, Mohammad Tarique, and Sharique Zafar. "Temperament of Drugs in Unani Medicine: A Critical Analysis." *Hamdard Medicus* 55.3 (2012).

Albala, Ken. *Eating Right in the Renaissance*. Berkeley, CA: University of California Press, 1964.

Arikha, Noga. *Passions and Tempers a History of the Humours*. New York: Ecco, 2007.

Alchindus, De Gradibus Medicinarum Compositaru, attributed to Arnald De Villanova (1234–1310).

Avicenna. *Canon of Medicine, Book II Materia Medica*. New Delhi, India: Hamdard University, 1998.

Barthlomaeus Anglicus. *On the Properties of Things*. Translated by John Trevisa. 3 Vols. Oxford: Claredon Press, 1975.

Bartlett, Robert Allen. *Real Alchemy*. Lake Worth, FL: Ibis, 2009.

Becker, Christian August. *Das Aceton*. 1867. Translated by Shuck and Nintzel. Richardson, TX: Restorers of Alchemical Manuscripts, 1981.

Chishti, G. M. *The Traditional Healers Handbook: A Classic Guide to the Medicine of Avicenna*. Rochester, VT: Healing Arts Press, 1988.

Coppens, Filip, and Hans Vymazalová. "Medicine, Mathematics and Magic Unite in a Scene from the Temple of Kom Ombo (KO 950)." *Anthropologie* 48.2-3 (2010): 9–13.

Culpeper, Nicholas. *Pharmacopoeia Londinensis*. Boston, 1720.

De Fourcroy, Antoine. *Elements of Natural History and of Chemistry*, Vol. 4. London: Printed for G. G. J. and J. Robinson, Pater Noster Row, 1788.

DeGroot, F., William, Wei Ping Pan, M. Dalilur Rahman, Geoffrey Richards. "First Chemical Events in Pyrolysis of Wood." Journal of Analytical and Applied Pyrolisis 13.3 (1988): 221–31.

de Wild, Paul, Hans Reith, and Erik Heeres. "Biomass Pyrolysis for Chemicals." Biofuels 2.2 (2011): 185–208.

Floyer, John. *Pharmako-Basanos or The Touch-stone of Medicines*. Vol.1. London, 1687.

French, John. *The Art of Distillation*. London, 1651. Reprint: San Francisco, CA: Para Publishers, 1978.

Ghayas, Syma. *Identification and Determination of Humors in the Blood Applying Clinical and Conventional Laboratory Techniques*. Thesis to, Hamdard University. Karachi, India, 2009.

Glaser, Christopher. *The Complete Chymist*. 1677. Richardson, TX: Restorers of Alchemical Manuscripts, 1983.

Glauber, Johann Rudolf. *The Complete Works of Rudolf Glauber*. Translated by Christopher Packe. Boulder, CO, 1983.

Grant, Mark. *Galen on Food and Diet*. London: Routledge, 2000.

Greenbaum, Dorian Gieseler. *Temperament: Astrology's Forgotten Key*. Bournemouth, UK: The Wessex Astrologer, 2005.

Grew, Nehemiah. *The Anatomy of Plants*. London: The Royal Society, 1682.

Haq, Syed Nomanul. *Names, Natures and Things*. Boston Studies in the Philosophy of Science, Vol. 158. Springer, 1994.

Hartmann, Franz. *The Life and Doctrines of Paracelsus*. Los Angeles: Mokulume Hill Press, 1972.

Hippocrates. *The Aphorisms of Hippocrates*. Translated by Elias Marks. New York: Collins, 1817.

————. The Loeb Classical Library Vol. 4. Translated by W. H. S. Jones. Cambridge, MA: Harvard University Press, 1954.

Holland, Isaac. *A Compendium of Writings by Johan Isaaci Hollandus*. Translated by RAMS. Richardson, TX: Restorers of Alchemical Manuscripts, 1981.

Holmyard, Eric John. "Medieval Arabic Pharmacology." *Proceedings of the Royal Society of Medicine* 29 (1935): 99–108.

Huguet-Termes, Teresa. Islamic Pharmacology in the Latin West: An Approach to Early Pharmacopeias. European Review 16 No.

2, 2008 p. 229–239.

Hunter, Michael, "Boyle versus the Galenists: A Suppressed Critique of Seventeenth-Century Medical Practice and its Significance." *Medical History* 41.3 (1997): 322–361.

Hurley, Phillip. *Herbal Alchemy*. Chicago: Lotus, 1977.

Jacquart, Danielle. "Islamic Pharmacology in the Middle Ages: Theories and Substances." *European Review* 16.2 (2008): 219–27.

Junius, Manfred M. *The Practical Handbook of Plant Alchemy*. New York: Inner Traditions, 1985.

Kirchweger, Anton. *The Golden Chain of Homer*. Translated from the German 1781 Rosicrucian edition by RAMS. Richardson, TX.

Krause, Paul. "Jābirian Alchemy (A Translation of the Introduction and Chapter One, Section One of *Jābir Ibn Ḥayyān: Contribution to the History of Scientific Ideas in Islam: Jābir and Greek Science*)," International Journal of Shīʿī Studies 4.2 (2006): 195–220. Translated from French by Keven Brown.

LeBlanc, Jeffery. *Slow Pyrolysis Experiments For High Yields of Solid Carbon*. PhD. Dissertation. New York: City College of New York, 2016.

Lemery, Nicholas. *Course of Chymistry*. London, 1698.

Levey, M. *Early Arabic Pharmacology, An Introduction based on Ancient and Medieval Sources*. Leiden: Brill, 1973.

Lloyd, G. E. R., ed. *Hippocratic Writings*. Harmondsworth, NY: Penguin, 1978.

McVaugh, Michael R. "Quantified Medical Theory and Practice at Fourteenth-Century Montpellier." *Bulletin of the History of Medicine* 43.5 (1969): 397–413.

Mones Abu-Asab, Hakima Amri, Marc S. Micozzi. *Avicenna's Medicine*. Rochester, VT: Healing Arts Press, 2013.

Morrison, Robert. "Musa Calinus' Treatise on the Natures of Medicines and Their Use." *Nazariyat Journal for the History of Islamic Philosophy and Sciences* 3.1 (2006): 77–136.

Newman, William R. *Promethean Ambitions: Alchemy and the Quest to Perfect Nature*. Chicago: University of Chicago Press, 2004.

——— . *Atoms and Alchemy: Chymistry and the Experimental Origins of the Scientific Revolution* Chicago: University of Chicago Press, 2006.

Nunn, John F. *Ancient Egyptian Medicine*. Norman, OK: University of Oklahoma Press, 1996.

Nutton, Vivian. *Ancient Medicine*. London: Routledge, 2004.

Paracelsus. *The Hermetic and Alchemical Writings of Paracelsus*. Edited by A. E. Waite. James Elliot, 1894. Reprint: London: University Books, 1967.

——— . *Volumen Medicinae Paramirum*. Translated by Kurt F. Leidecker. Baltimore: The Johns Hopkins Press, 1949.

Peters, Hermann. *Pictorial History of Ancient Pharmacy*. Translated by Dr. William Netter. Chicago: G. P. Engelhard, 1899.

Pommerening, Tanja. "Healing Measures: dja and oipe in Ancient Egyptian Pharmacy and Medicine," 132–37, in J. Cockitt and R. Davies (eds.), *Pharmacy and Medicine in Ancient Egypt: proceedings of the Conferences Held in Cairo (2007) and Manchester (2008)* (Oxford: Archaeopress, 2010).

Ptolemy, Claudius. *Tetrabiblos*. Translated by J. M. Ashmand. Davis and Dickson. London, 1822.

Ramezany, Farid, et.al. "Primary Qualities in Phytotherapy and Traditional Medicines: A Statistical Study." *Journal of Drug Delivery and Therapeutics* 3.3 (2013): 1–6.

Regimen sanitatis Salernitanum. Trans. Thomas Paynell. 1528.

Ricordel, Joelle. "Compound Medicine: Andalusian Theories on the Evaluation of its Degree (Twelfth Century)." *History of Pharmacy Review* 89.330 (2001): 135–48.

Saunders, Richard. *The Astrological Judgment and Practice of Physick*. 1677. Bel Air, MD: Astrology Classics, 2005.

Savage-Smith, Emilie. "Medicine in Medieval Islam," 2:139–67, in *The Cambridge History of Science*. Eds. Michael H. Shank and David C. Lindberg (Cambridge: Cambridge University Press, 2013).

——— . "Were the Four Humours Fundamental to Medieval Islamic Medical Practice?" 89–106, in: Peregrine Horden and Elisabeth Hsu, eds., *The Body in Balance: Humoral Medicines in Practice* (New York: Berghan Books, 2015).

Scarborough, John, "XIII Early Byzantine Pharmacology", 213–32, in John Scarborough, *Pharmacy and Drug Lore in Antiquity: Greece, Rome, Byzantium* (Farnham, VT: Ashgate Variorum, 2010).

Sendivogius, Michael. *The New Chemical Light*. 1608. Richardson, TX: Restorers of Alchemical Manuscripts, 1982.

Sennert, Daniel. *Nine Books of Physick and Chirurgy*. London, 1676.

Siddiqi, Tazimuddin. "Ibn Sina on Materia Medica." *Indian Journal of History of Science* 21.4 (1986): 326–57.

Smith, Wesley, D. *The Hippocratic Tradition*. Ithaca, NY: Cornell University Press 1979. Revised electronic edition 2002

Stelmack, Robert, M. and Anastasios Stalikas. "Galen on the Humour Theory of Temperament." *Personality and Individual Differences* 12.3 (1991): 255–63.

Thorndike, Lynn. *A History of Magic and Experimental Science*, 8 Vols. New York: Columbia University Press, 1923–1958.

Tobyn, Graeme. *Culpeper's Medicine*. Philadelphia, PA: Singing Dragon, 1997.

Tzvi Langermann, Y., "Another Andalusian revolt? Ibn Rushd's critique of al-Kindī's pharmacological computus", 351–72, in: Jan P. Hogendijk and Abdelhamid I. Sabra, *The Enterprise of Science in Islam. New Perspectives* (Cambridge, MA: MIT Press, 2003).

Valentine, Basil. *Triumphal Chariot of Antimony* with annotations of Theodore Kerckring. Printed for Dorman Newman at the Kings Arms in the Poultry, 1678. Photocopy of original edition.

———. *The Last Will and Testament of Basil Valentine*. Printed by S. G. and B. G. for Edward Brewster, and to be sold at the Sign of the Crane in St. Paul's Churchyard ,1672.

van Arsdall, Anne and Timothy Graham, eds. *Herbs and Healers from the Ancient Mediterranean Through the Medieval West*. London: Routledge, 2012.

Weidenfeld, Johannes Segerus. *Secrets of the Adepts*. 1685. Reprint: Richardson, TX: Restorers of Alchemical Manuscripts, 1982.

THE TEMPER OF HERBS

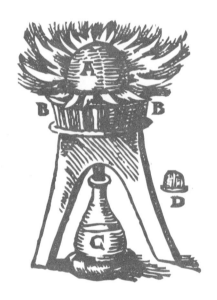

The Temper of Herbs was typeset in Signifier, Stella, Miniscule, Alpina, Genath, and Flecha by Joseph Uccello of the Viatorium Press. The first, limited print run of 666 copies features gold foil on the cover, and is only available directly through the publisher, while supplies last. *The Temper of Herbs* is also available as an eBook. While no audio book exists as of this printing, a recording of Robert A. Bartlett presenting this research at the third annual Viridis Genii Symposium in Damascus, Oregon in 2017, is for sale at viridisgenii.com.

CPSIA information can be obtained
at www.ICGtesting.com
Printed in the USA
BVHW021730240222
630016BV00011B/533